A Plan to Save the Planet

By Glenn Weinreb

How to resolve climate change at the lowest cost and in a way that is politically feasible

Published Dec 1, 2022 | v9m2
Copyright © 2022 by Glenn Weinreb
Glenn Weinreb Press | Cambridge, MA, USA

ISBN 979-8-9873895-2-2   eBook/Kindle
      979-8-9873895-0-8   Hardcover
      979-8-9873895-1-5   Paperback B&N, Amazon
      979-8-218-10625-6   Paperback Ingram

Table of Contents

Note from Author

Forty years ago I started a company that designs and manufactures products that automate factories and research laboratories.

And over forty years, almost every day, I interacted with manufacturing engineers and research scientists at thousands of different organizations.

Also, I have profited from carbon. For example, I sold approximately $5 million worth of the device shown here to the petroleum industry. I love what carbon has done for us. Without it, we and our cities would not be here.

Also, carbon's place in history will eventually come to an end.

Like the sun setting on a hot summer day.

Helping the Planet is more Fun than Making Money

One morning in 2019, I awoke with an epiphany. I felt my job was meaningless and wanted to do something different. I was tired of chasing money as an entrepreneur, and was thrilled by the idea of instead helping the planet using the skills I'd developed over forty years.

I thought about how my background was unique and gave me a different perspective on energy, manufacturing, and R&D. So I formed a non-profit with some friends called The Manhattan 2 Project. And between 2019 and 2022, I sponsored and managed 25 university R&D students, and published 30 articles on climate change solutions. I have published more than anyone else in the electronics industry on this topic.

For a TEDx talk that summarizes this book in 10 minutes, search "a plan to save the planet" at TED.com. And for a CBS news segment that discusses some of my work, search "sesL3id7hba" at YouTube.com.

Contact the Author

To contact Glenn Weinreb, email gWeinreb (at) manhattan2.org

Footnotes and References

The electronic version of this book provides links to references. Also, an on-line open-source spreadsheet contains dozens of pages of calculations and links to more references.

Acknowledgments

We would like to thank Dr. Maurizio Di Paolo Emilio for editing material previously published in EETimes.com and PowerElectronicsNews.com. This book reprints some of this with the permission of publisher AspenCore.

Preface

This is the first book ever that explains how to resolve climate change at the lowest cost and in a way that is politically feasible. In essence, a plan to save the planet.

The easiest solution is a federal law that requires decarbonization over 30 years, with additional costs passed onto consumers. If applied to the U.S., this would cost each American $20 in year #1, $40 in year #2, $60 in year #3, etc.

The world's current economic decarbonization strategy is to encourage individuals, companies, cities, and regions to reduce CO_2 emissions. However, they rarely have the physical ability to do so at the lowest cost. Instead, we should task power companies with decarbonizing at massive scales.

Decarbonization policy in the U.S. is controlled by a political coalition of environmentalists, labor unions, and the automobile industry. Unfortunately, labor and auto must focus on their own financial interests, and not getting to zero at the lowest cost. To do the latter, one would need a political coalition that benefits. For example, regions that import carbon-based fuels benefit from lowest-cost decarbonization in two ways: (a) they gain local green jobs while carbon jobs are lost elsewhere, and (b) they save money when decarbonization causes fuel price to drop, due to less fuel consumption.

The cherry on top of our climate solutions sundae is a new R&D laboratory that further reduces decarbonization costs.

1.   The Climate War

The climate war entails a battle between those who want to stop putting CO_2 into the atmosphere and those who don't. Those who want to stop are concerned about harm to the world's ecosystems, food shortages in a dryer world, more severe storms, and a rising sea level. Those who are against decarbonization either believe it is unimportant, or prefer someone else be inconvenienced. Less convenience ranges from paying more for a green product to losing a carbon-based job.

Decarbonization in the United States

The most interesting climate change graph is the U.S. government's official projection of CO_2 emissions over the next 30 years.

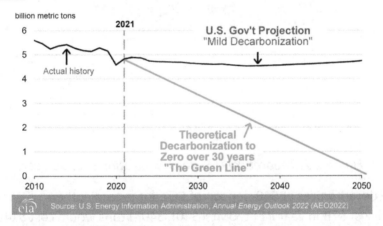

Figure 1.1: U.S. government's official projection of CO_2 emissions from the U.S. over the next 30 years in units of billions of tons each year

This graph is updated every year, and as one can see, the U.S. is not decarbonizing. Our failure is due to the fact that our economic and political decarbonization strategies are fundamentally wrong, as we will discuss later.

The Green Line

A Green Line in the above graph is a projection of what it would look like to fully decarbonize over the next 30 years at a constant rate. This book is about that Line. Chapter 3 explores how much this Line would cost consumers, Chapter 6 looks at who blocks the Line, and Chapters 8 through

12 explores how to deal with them. This book focuses on the United States; however, other countries have similar climate change issues.

How much does the Green Line Cost?

The U.S. emits approximately 5 billion tons of CO_2 each year. If this dropped to zero at a constant rate over 30 years, it would decrease by 170 million tons each year. This is because 5 billion divided by 30 is 170 million.

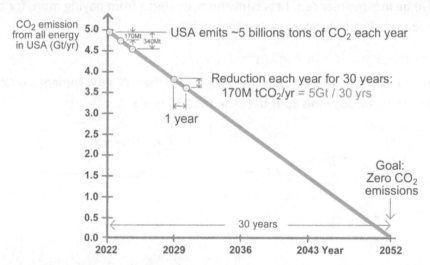

Figure 1.2: Theoretical U.S. decarbonization over 30 years.

If one decarbonizes at $40-per-ton of CO_2, for example, then 170M tons would cost $7B in year #1 (170Mt x $40), 340M tons would cost $14B in year #2, etc. This would cost each U.S. citizen $20 in year #1 ($7B / 330M population), $40 in year #2, etc. In the typical case, this would pay the mortgage on new solar farms, minus the cost of carbon-based fuel that was not burned due to being replaced with green electricity. Ultimately, these expenses would appear as an increase in the cost of goods and services.

	Year 1	Year 2	Year 3
Cost/Person/Yr	$20	$40	$60
CO_2 Reduced	170M tons	340M tons	510M tons

Federal Law That Does the Green Line

To implement the Green Line at the lowest cost, one would need a simple federal law with two provisions.

1. Require 6% of electricity to be decarbonized each year over a period of 9 years.

2. Set up an R&D laboratory tasked with reducing decarbonization costs.

Approximately 38% of U.S. electricity is currently generated without emitting CO_2. If this is increased by 6% each year, then 44% would be green after year #1, 50% would be green after year #2, etc.

To decarbonize at the lowest cost, power companies would need to replace carbon-based electricity with solar, wind, hydro and nuclear power.

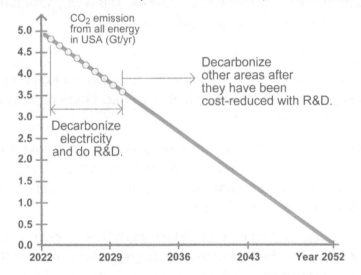

Figure 1.3: Decarbonize electricity first, while reducing other decarbonization costs with R&D.

Our Green Line has two parts. The first 9 years are achieved mostly with electricity decarbonization. And the following 21 years are cost-reduced with R&D during the first 9 years. At this time, electricity is the only area that is ready to decarbonize at massive scales, at low cost, and with government monitoring.

Our Current Economic Strategy is Fundamentally Wrong

The world's current economic decarbonization strategy is to encourage individuals, companies, cities, and states to reduce CO_2 emissions. At first glance, this seems reasonable. However, it is flawed since these entities rarely have the physical ability to do this at the lowest cost. This is like asking a city mayor to build a car from scratch in the local shop. Can he do it? Yes. However, it might cost him 100 times more than factory mass production. Instead, the mayor should let the automobile industry handle mass production in the same way we should let power companies decarbonize at massive sales.

Here's another example. Imagine trying to place 20 solar panels onto a million different homes. One would incur project overhead cost a million times (e.g. customer acquisition, system design, permitting, inspection, etc.). Alternatively, if one installs 20 million panels at a large solar farm, they would not see overhead every 20 panels. This is why solar farm cost-per-unit-electricity is 3-times less than residential solar.

Climate Change Politics in the U.S.

There are two kinds of regions -- those that produce and export carbon-based fuels, and those that import fuels. One might think of these as *fuel exporters* and *fuel importers*.

There is only one thing you need to know about climate change politics. Regions that produce a fuel will not politically support eliminating it. If one understands this, they will understand what is happening politically with climate change, and understand how to fix it.

For example, regions that produce natural gas will not support fully replacing natural gas-based electricity with green electricity. And the same is true with coal and oil.

The maps below indicate where fuels are produced in the U.S.

Fortunately, two-thirds of states do not produce natural gas or coal.

Figure 1.4: U.S. suppliers of oil, coal and natural gas.

Importers of Carbon Fuel Benefit from Decarbonization

Fuel *exporters* are hurt by decarbonization. However, the opposite is true for *importers*. They benefit in two ways:

1. Local green jobs are created when nearby wind and solar farms are constructed. This occurs while carbon jobs are lost elsewhere.

2. Money is saved when decarbonization causes fuel prices to decrease, due to less fuel consumption, due to decarbonization.

Our Current Political Strategy is Fundamentally Wrong

Existing decarbonization legislation in the U.S. was drafted by a political coalition of environmentalist, labor unions and the automobile industry. At first glance, this might seem reasonable. However, it is fundamentally flawed since labor and auto must focus on their own financial interests, not getting to zero at the lowest cost.

Alternatively, to decarbonize electricity at the lowest cost, one would need a coalition of lawmakers that benefit from exactly that, lowest-cost electricity decarbonization. This is not labor or auto. Instead, this would be the two-thirds of the U.S. states that import natural gas and coal.

A Website to Save the Planet

Suppose a region is considering decarbonizing X% of electricity each year over a period of Y years. To assess the impact, one would need to calculate: (a) lowest cost approach, (b) amount of CO_2 reduced, (c) cost per ton of CO_2 reduced, (d) cost per person per year, (e) savings due to lower fuel price, (f) number of jobs gained and lost, and their locations.

Currently, this information is not easily obtained. Therefore, a website is needed that calculates it after the user specifies X, Y, and region.

Doing detailed modeling for all nations, regions, and metropolitan areas worldwide might cost on the order of $100 million. However, without this website, lowest-cost global decarbonization might be impossible.

The Manhattan 2 Project

When there is a problem, someone is typically tasked with resolving it in some way. However, with climate change, no one seems to own the entire problem. And this is one reason why we formed The Manhattan 2 Project in 2019. CEO Victor Colantonio and I were convinced that someone needed to own the entire problem. This might seem overly burdensome. However, that is not the case since it just means we do research on how to resolve climate change at the lowest cost, and in a way that is politically feasible.

In other words, develop a plan to save the planet.

This book is that plan.

You Can Save the Planet Too!

Governments, foundations and researchers can develop plans to save the planet too. To make this easier, this book's original Microsoft Word file, spreadsheets, and illustrations are available to copy and modify for free at www.APlanToSaveThePlanet.org/open. To the author's knowledge, the concepts discussed are public knowledge and no patents are pending.

You can save the planet too!

Decarbonization Advocacy

If the reader is interested in participating in the democratic process, consider sending a letter to a government representative. For an example, visit www.APlanToSaveThePlanet.org/easiest-pathway

Always Begin with Plan

Plan writing forces one to break a problem down into component parts, put together a solution for each, and make sure each solution is feasible. With climate change, this entails putting together an economic strategy, a political strategy, and a technical strategy.

Economic strategy involves decarbonizing at the lowest cost. Political strategy involves groups that have at least 51% political support who benefit from lowest-cost decarbonization. And technical strategy involves reducing decarbonization costs with more R&D.

The world has not had a plan to tackle climate change in the past, and this has led to wasted time and money.

Business and engineering schools teach "Always begin with a plan".

We should apply this to climate change.

2. Climate Change Math

This chapter is a brief review of the physics involved in climate change.

Electricity in a Nutshell

A watt (W) is a unit of electrical power, and a watt flowing over a period of time is a unit of energy. For example, one thousand watts flowing for one hour is a kilowatt-hour (1kWh), and one trillion watts flowing for one hour is a terawatt-hour (1TWh).

Total electricity consumption during 2021 was 8,500 TWh in China, 4,200 TWh in the U.S., and 1,700 TWh in India (BP Review, 2021).

The typical U.S. home consumes 10,000 kWh of electricity each year at an average cost of 14¢ per kilowatt-hour (14¢/kWh, EIA, May 2021). This is the retail price, and it includes the cost of generation and distribution. Alternatively, the wholesale price refers to a large volume at the front gate of a power generation facility.

"Green" electricity does not emit CO_2 and is primarily generated by solar panels, wind farms, hydroelectric dams, and nuclear power plants. This typically costs 3¢ to 6¢ per kWh wholesale. Alternatively, carbon-based electricity is generated by burning coal or natural gas at a typical wholesale cost of 2¢ to 4¢ per kWh.

Consumers often receive a blend of green and carbon-based electricity. For example, if 20% is 4¢ green electricity, and 80% is 3¢ natural gas-based electricity, the blend would cost 3.2¢ per kWh ((20% x 4¢) + (80% x 3¢)).

Power company engineers are tasked with providing electricity at lowest cost, independent of CO_2. They do this unless given further instructions from government or customers who can request greener electricity, even if it cost more.

CO_2 in a Nutshell

Quantities of carbon dioxide gas (CO_2) are defined by their weight. For example, one metric ton (1 $mtCO_2$) and one billion metric tons (1 $GtCO_2$) both refer to CO_2 quantities. For reference, one metric ton is 1000 kilograms (2,204LBs) and one short ton is 2,000Lbs (907kg).

The typical U.S. gas car emits <u>4.6</u> metric tons of CO_2 each year (4.6mtCO$_2$/yr). And the typical U.S. home emits 4.1 metric tons each year due to electricity consumption (4.1mtCO$_2$/yr).

In most countries, the lowest cost way to make electricity is to burn coal, and this emits <u>1kg</u> (2.2LBs) of CO_2 for each kWh of electricity. Alternatively, one can burn natural gas, and emit 0.4kg (0.9LBs) of CO_2 per kWh.

Annual <u>CO_2 emissions</u> are 10 billion tons from China, 5 billion tons from America, and 2.5 billion tons from India. Approximately one-third is due to making electricity with natural gas and coal, one-third from pushing vehicles with gasoline and diesel fuel, and one-third from making heat within factories and buildings with natural gas and coal.

Worldwide, CO_2 emissions keep <u>going up</u>, as shown below.

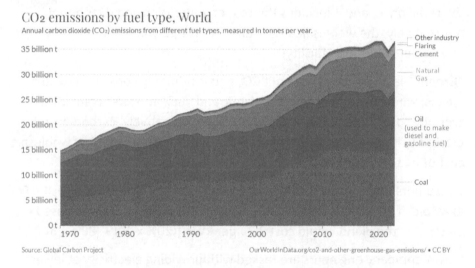

Figure 2.1: Global CO_2 emissions over the last 50 years.

The Problem with CO_2

The Earth is an 8,000 mile (13K km) diameter sphere covered by a <u>60</u> miles (100 km) thick atmosphere. Incoming radiation from the sun passes through the atmosphere as it travels toward land. And outgoing radiation from the land travels in the opposite direction toward outer space.

The Earth gets warmer if outgoing radiation decreases, or incoming radiation increases. And radiation decreases if it bumps into molecules in the atmosphere that deflect. Also, the type of outgoing radiation is different than the type of incoming radiation. And the outgoing type deflects more easily.

Scientists approximately 100 years ago placed different gases and different types of radiation into desk-sized laboratory chambers and measured deflection. They observed some molecules and some types of radiation deflect more than others. For example, greenhouse gases such as CO_2 and CH_4 (methane) deflect more than the typical air molecule.

When a photon travels through the atmosphere, it passes approximately 300,000,000 air molecules *each meter* as it travels 100,000 meters. The photon only needs to bump into one molecule along its path to deflect. For this reason, a relatively small amount of CO_2 can have an impact.

The Food Problem

Additional heat causes land to dry out. And dryer soil often produces less food. When people do not have enough food, they typically move to areas with more food. And this can lead to overcrowding, shortages, and high prices. The wealthy buy what they need when prices are high, while the poor struggle. And this can lead to social unrest, more police, and gated communities. We are observing some of this already, in part due to climate change. However, it is unclear when, where and how it will get worse.

Migration does not necessarily need to be a problem. If the rate of adding food production and housing is greater than the rate of adding population, then shortages and high prices are less likely.

The Tipping Points Problem

Another problem with CO_2 is the possibility that a not well-understood positive feedback loop will make the situation worse than expected. For example, thawing permafrost could potentially release greenhouse gas methane more than expected. And this could lead to more warming and more thawing.

The Sea Level Rise Problem

Eventually our civilization will stop putting CO_2 into the atmosphere and the planet will stop warming. However, after we stop emitting CO_2, the additional temperature will hover for thousands of years as the CO_2 slowly falls back to earth, and the temperature slowly reverts back to its original level.

As the elevated temperature hovers for thousands of years, it will slowly melt a 2000 meter-thick slab of ice on Antarctica (i.e. the South Pole). And this will cause the sea to rise and cover coastal cities. Sea level is expected to rise slowly. Perhaps one to two meters every 100 years. However, after 30 to 300 years, this will be a problem for many coastal areas.

A *Quickly Changing* Planet is a Bad Planet

In theory, civilization could move to areas that are more suitable. However, this entails a race between a changing planet, and the builders of metropolitan areas. If the planet changed faster than the civilization could build, there would be suffering.

The degree of suffering is likely to be proportional to the rate of planet changing, not the absolute amount. For example, if it takes 1000 years to flood coastal cities, and each building lasts 100 years, then new buildings would probably not be built in areas that are flooded in their lifetime.

It is not clear *when* we will stop putting CO_2 into the atmosphere. The alarm bells started to ring about 10 years ago, and some progress has been made. However, political support for legislation that requires decarbonization has been missing. And this is in part due to: (a) the political strength of the fossil fuel industry, (b) the lack of websites that model the impact and cost of decarbonization initiatives, (c) and the failure of political leaders to recognize that real decarbonization (i.e. the Green Line) is likely to be driven by a coalition of lawmakers from regions that do not produce carbon-based fuels.

3.   The Decarbonization Act of 202x (proposed)

This chapter provides an example of a U.S. federal law that would implement the Green Line at the lowest cost.

The U.S. Decarbonization Act of 202x (proposed)

1. CO_2 emissions from <u>human activity</u> are *required* to decrease to zero, over 30 years, at a constant rate, at the lowest cost, and in lowest cost order (i.e. follow the Green Line).

2. U.S. electricity is *required* to decarbonize at 6% per year, over a period of 9 years, at lowest cost. For example, 38% of electricity is made without emitting CO_2 today, 44% after year #1, 50% after year #2, etc.

3. A new R&D laboratory is set up to further reduce decarbonization costs.

How Much Would This Cost?

Currently, <u>38.4%</u> of U.S. electricity is made without emitting CO_2 and if this were to increase 6% each year for 9 years, then 92% would be green after nine years (38.4% + 6% x 9yrs).

The U.S. produces <u>4,100TWh</u> of electricity each year and if 6% of this were decarbonized each year, then approximately 246TWh of coal and natural gas-based electricity would be replaced with solar, wind, hydro and nuclear each year (4,100 x 6%).

Currently, <u>38%</u> of U.S. electricity is made with natural gas, and 22% is made with coal. If 246TWh/yr were divided by these proportions, then 157TWh of natural gas and 89TWh of coal would be replaced with green electricity each year. Subsequently, CO_2 would decrease 65Mt/yr due to burning less natural gas, and decrease 90Mt/yr due to burning less coal (millions of metric tons per year). Total CO_2 reduction would be 154Mt/yr (65 + 90) and this would satisfy 90% of the 170Mt/yr requirement (154 / 170).

If half of the carbon-based electricity were decarbonized by constructing solar farms and half by constructing wind farms, for example, then 53GW of solar would be constructed each year, and 32GW of wind would be constructed each year. This is approximately 4-times more than the average between 2016 and 2021. The solar TWh-to-GW ratio is different than the wind ratio, since the wind blows more than the sun shines.

If decarbonization costs increased from $10/mtCO_2$ to $50/mtCO_2$ over a 9 year period (cost to reduce CO_2 by one metric ton), for example, then the cost of residential electricity would increase $1 per-person-per-year in year #1.

Sounds too good to be true? Total cost for year #1 would be $1.54B (154Mt x $10/mtCO_2$), total electricity cost-per-person-per-year would be $5 ($1.54B / 330M population), and *residential* electricity cost-per-person-per-year would be $1 ($5 x 20%). We apply 20% since 1/5th of all electricity is residential.

The table below shows what this looks like for the first four years. This analysis assumes inflation and GDP growth are zero to make this easier to follow.

		Year #1	Year #2	Year #3	Year #4
Decarbonization Cost	$/mtCO_2$	$10	$15	$20	$25
% U.S. Electricity Decarbonized	%	44%	50%	56%	62%
Decarbonization "Mortgages"	$B/yr	$1.5	$1.5	$1.5	$1.5
US NREL, LCOE, 2022, Class 4	"		$2.3	$2.3	$2.3
	"			$3.1	$3.1
	"				$3.9
Total cost	$B/yr	$1.5	$3.9	$6.9	$10.8
Total cost for residential electricity (20%)	$B/yr	$0.3	$0.8	$1.4	$2.2
Cost of residential electricity per person	$/yr	$0.9	$2.3	$4.2	$6.5

Table 1: Calculated electricity decarbonization costs.

If one did not decarbonize in the lowest cost order and instead incurred $50/mtCO_2$ costs in year #1, then the total electricity cost-per-person-per-year in year #1 would be $25 instead of $5.

Getting it done at the Lowest Cost

About 40% of all U.S. CO_2 emissions are from making electricity and 60% are from burning carbon-based fuels to produce heat and force within vehicles, factories and buildings. If one wanted to decarbonize all energy over 30 years at the lowest cost, one might first focus on electricity, and decarbonize other areas after they had been cost-reduced via R&D. In other words, spend as little money as possible each year, over 30 years, while reducing CO_2 emissions by $1/30^{th}$ of today's emissions each year.

A strategy like this would result in constructing significantly more solar farms and wind farms. Yet how does one do that?

What Drives Solar/Wind Farm Construction?

The number of solar farms and wind farms built each year is primarily determined by the following factors:

i. **Government Requirements:** Legislation that requires power companies to generate more green electricity each year (e.g. RPS).

ii. **Government Subsidies**: Legislation that provides government money to help pay for green electricity to reduce its effective price (e.g. ITC).

iii. **Cost of Green Electricity:** Cost to generate green electricity (¢/kWh).

iv. **Cost of Carbon Fuel:** Cost of natural gas and coal fuel that are burned to produce carbon-based electricity (¢/kWh).

v. **Green Consumerism:** The number of consumers willing to pay more for green products.

In the above list, (i) and (ii) are controlled by lawmakers, (iii) improves each year due to technology and production advancements, (iv) varies up and down due to external factors, and (v) increases as climate change harm becomes more obvious.

Increase Solar Farm and Wind Farm Construction

To increase the rate of electricity decarbonization, one would need more of the above listed items. For example, U.S. federal *subsidies* on green electricity are approximately 1¢/kWh as of Sept 2022, and if these doubled, the affect would be significant. In another example, Massachusetts *requires* 35% of its electricity to be green by 2030. Other states are similar. However, these targets would need to be significantly higher to decarbonize over a reasonable period of time.

Climate Change Policy Options

Policy options can reduce decarbonization costs. Below are several examples.

- Establish a government office with authority to amend electricity purchase agreements between electricity customers and carbon-based power plants, so that customers can more easily replace carbon-based electricity with green electricity.

- Establish a government office with authority to *replace* existing power transmission lines with larger lines on a wider tract of land. For details, see the "Automate the Construction of Power Line Towers" chapter.

- Set up a green energy production zone program where communities voluntarily join to increase economic activity. In these zones, land-owners have the right to build solar farms and wind farms, a government office has the authority to demand right of way for new power transmission lines, etc.

Decarbonization Anxiety

Required decarbonization is scary is two ways:

Cost Anxiety: It is reasonable to be afraid of decarbonization costs, especially when nations rarely decarbonize at lowest cost. For this reason, decarbonization law that requires lowest cost, and websites that calculate costs, are important.

Carbon Industry Anxiety: It is reasonable for regions with many carbon-based industries to be afraid of the social and economic pain associated with downsizing. One should not expect political support from these regions when doing the Green Line.

4. The U.S. National Decarbonization Laboratory (proposed)

The U.S. government currently operates dozens of national laboratories, an example of which is the Jet Propulsion Laboratory (JPL) in California. They develop gadgets that explore outer space with a $3B/yr budget.

Figure 4.1: Jet Propulsion Laboratory in California, USA.

In theory, the U.S. government could do something similar with climate change by setting up a new national laboratory that develops gadgets that reduce decarbonization costs.

Foundations could also set up laboratories. For example, Bill could set up a Gates Decarbonization Laboratory, and Elon could set up a Musk Decarbonization Laboratory. And these could collaborate with Joe's U.S. National Decarbonization Laboratory.

What Do Labs Do?

Some laboratories develop large systems, whereas others focus on supporting research via grants. For example, JPL focuses on developing large systems such as the Mars rover, and the National Renewable Energy Laboratory (NREL) is active in supporting research grants.

The typical grant process is as follows: (a) announce funding opportunity, (b) collect proposals, (c) review, (d) select, and (e) manage awardees.

Organizational Structure

Laboratories typically divide responsibility among multiple divisions, and divisions typically divide responsibility among multiple groups. Panels of individuals allocate money from a general fund to divisions and to groups. And staff are encouraged to raise money from external sources via proposals.

Some laboratories have many employees at one site, whereas others funnel money toward other organizations. For example, a laboratory that accelerates the development of fusion power might pass money to scientists at the world's 10 fusion research organizations who are already familiar with fusion.

Foundations, Companies, and Universities

Companies and universities who receive money for R&D often prioritize their own financial interests over reducing CO_2. For example, they typically do not share developed materials unless they are required to do so. This is because transparency often detracts from: (a) filing patents, (b) developing proprietary products, and (c) raising money for companies and labs.

A decarbonization laboratory, on the other hand, might be tasked with solving the climate change problem, and not with making money. And to do this, they might require developed materials be placed onto the internet, open source. This would maximize the utilization of developed technology, maximize candid review, maximize the development of interconnection standards, and minimize inaccurate claims.

Laboratory Divisions

A new laboratory could have any number of divisions, and it could add or subtract at any time. Below are examples of divisions.

Commercial Fusion: Accelerate the development of fusion power. Possibly tasked with achieving commercial fusion within 5 to 10 years. Funding is directed by the world's top fusion scientists and flows toward top people at existing fusion research institutions.[1, 2, 3, 25]

Safer Fission Power: Make nuclear fission power safer, to the extent required by the public. Funding is directed by the world's top fission scientists and flows toward top people at existing fission research institutions.[4, 5, 6, 7, 24]

High-Temperature Manufacturing: Develop next-generation high-temperature green manufacturing sites, standards, and supporting transportation infrastructure.[4, 5, 6, 7, 26]

Custom Solar Skin: Develop machines that fabricate, install and maintain custom pieces of PV solar material that wrap building roof and wall surfaces.[8, 31]

Solar Sub-Assembly Development: Develop standardized modular solar sub-assembles that stack within a shipping container and are assembled under robotic control.[9, 32]

Solar Panel Installation Automation: Automate the placing of traditional solar panels on buildings.[9]

Solar Farm Automation: Develop next generation automated solar farms that consume significantly less metal, concrete, and glass.[10, 33]

The National Solar Farm: Develop an automated software system that supports ownership of solar panels on a solar farm.[29]

Ammonia Transportation: Do paper-only design of a global well-to-wheels ammonia based transportation system. This entails exploring ammonia-based fuel cells, ammonia tanks, automated refueling mechanisms, machines that automate the installation of underground infrastructure, and citywide ammonia monitoring and service.[11, 27, 28]

Hydrogen Transportation: Similar to the above yet hydrogen (H_2) instead of ammonia (NH_3).[11, 27, 28]

Electric Vehicle Cost Reduction: Reduce the cost of electric vehicles (EVs) to the extent required to make them cost less than gasoline and diesel powered vehicles. This includes improving EV battery longevity 2-fold (i.e. to beyond the lifespan of the vehicle), exploring dynamic battery warranty, and exploring mandated diagnostic battery reporting.[12, 13, 15, 28]

Swappable EV Battery: Develop a standardized swappable EV battery system, to the point of simple prototypes.[14, 28]

HEV Transportation: Support moving buyers from gas cars to HEVs (Hybrid, no plug, small electric motor and battery). HEVs cost ~$1.5K more than gas cars, get ~30% better gas mileage, and their additional cost is recovered within one to three years due to savings at the gas station.[15, 28]

HVAC Command and Control: Develop software and standards that connect HVAC equipment in all buildings to regional computers and to national computers. Support a national strategy that decarbonizes building space heating at lowest cost, and in a way that is likely to be supported by most voters.[16, 35]

Building Automation: Develop software, devices, and standards that automate buildings.[16, 17, 18, 19, 36]

Carbon Capture and Sequestration (CCS): Develop software, standards, systems, and models that support the eventual unfolding of CCS.[20, 30]

Power Line Transmission Automation and Commoditization: Reduce cost of electrical power transmission lines via automation and standardization.[21, 34]

Decarbonization Assessment: Grade public and private programs (e.g. carbon offsets) that reduce CO_2 according to decarbonization cost ($/mt$CO_2$), scientific validity, economic validity, prevalence of fraud, etc.[37]

Decarbonization Policy Making Tools: Maintain websites that calculate the lowest cost way for regions to decarbonize given policy options.[22, 23, 38]

Conclusion

More R&D could potentially reduce decarbonization costs. However, it is not easy to determine what, where and how to develop. Developing large systems is often avoided for a variety of reasons; however, one can explore with a relatively small budget. And requiring open source can help to avoid placing the entire system onto the shoulders of one organization.

Business schools teach that the best productivity comes from well-funded teams of outstanding individuals who are surrounded by minimal bureaucracy. Decarbonization laboratories that apply this principle would be more likely to be successful.

Decarbonization Laboratory Article References

[1] *How do we Accelerate the Development of Nuclear Fusion Power?*

Decarbonization Laboratory Chapter References

[24] "How do we Make Nuclear Fission Power Safer?" chapter

[25] "How do we Accelerate the Development of Fusion Power?" chapter

[26] "High-Temperature Green Manufacturing at Lowest Cost" chapter

[27] "The Economics of Green Fuel" chapter

[28] "Transportation is a 30 Trillion Dollar Problem" chapter

[29] "The National Solar Farm" chapter

[30] "Carbon, Capture and Sequestration" chapter

[31] "Cover Buildings with Solar Skin" chapter

[32] "Automate Solar on Buildings" chapter

[33] "Mechanize Solar on Land" chapter

[34] Chapter "Automate the Construction of Power Transmission Towers"

[35] "Decarbonize the Heating of Buildings" chapter

[36] "Develop Next Generation Buildings" chapter

[37] "Mild vs. Real Decarbonization" chapter

[38] "Fight Carbon with Websites" chapter

5. Mild Decarbonization vs. The Green Line

The U.S. Energy Information Administration (EIA) is an organization within the U.S. government that studies energy and CO_2 emissions. They expect CO_2 emissions over the next 30 years to remain approximately constant, as shown in the graph at the beginning of Chapter 1. In other words, according to the U.S. government, the U.S. is not reducing CO_2 emissions to zero. This projection is based on current government policy, and the fact that consumers buy the lowest cost solution. Other countries are similar with respect to decarbonization.

Projections are not Scenarios

The reader may have seen decarbonization *scenarios* that show CO_2 emissions dropping to zero over several decades. These show what would happen *if* decarbonization did occur, an example of which is the Green Line in Chapter 1. Alternatively, market *projections* reflect expected market behavior and existing government policy.

Projections do not assume government policy will change in the future, since policy would be different if lawmakers wanted it different. However, when and if policy does change, projections are updated. For example, the EIA's projection in Chapter 1 was calculated before the Inflation Reduction Act of 2022 (IRA) was passed in August of 2022. And later EIA projections will reflect the IRA, along with other factors such as fuel price changes.

Mild Decarbonization vs. the Green Line

In a sense, there are two types of decarbonization. Mild Decarbonization and the Green Line. Mild is when a relatively small amount of decarbonization occurs each year, and the Green Line is when one decarbonizes to zero over several decades. In the Chapter 1 graph, Mild is plotted in black, and the Green Line in green. Mild is what we are currently doing, and the Green Line is what we need to do to save the planet.

Many Nations do Mild Decarbonization

In the U.S., the amount of green electricity as a percentage of total increased from 35% to 37% over the last 5 years. In other words, U.S.

electricity is decarbonizing at a rate of 0.5% each year ((37.6% - 35.4%) / 4yrs). This is Mild Decarbonization.

Alternatively, if the U.S. fully decarbonized its electricity over 10 years, for example, this increase would be 6% each year ((100% - 38%) / 10yrs)). This would be Green Line decarbonization.

The U.S. is decarbonizing electricity at the pace of a snail. And other countries, like China, are similar.

Green Line Decarbonization

When decarbonizing, one can put money into brute-force decarbonization or R&D. Brute-force entails replacing carbon-based infrastructure with infrastructure that does not emit CO_2.

If 100% of infrastructure is replaced over 30 years at a constant rate, for example, then 3.3% would be replaced each year (100% / 30yrs). Gross Domestic Product (GDP) increases globally approximately 3% each year. Therefore, to keep up with GDP and decarbonize, one would need to build green at a rate of 6.3%/yr (3% + 3.3%). This is not happening, and this is one reason why we see global CO_2 emissions increasing.

Green infrastructure built over approximately 30 years worldwide is likely to cost approximately 100 trillion dollars. Approximately one-third for electrical power generation, one-third for transportation, and one-third for factories. In theory, R&D can reduce this cost.

Decarbonizing at Lowest Cost

To decarbonize at lowest cost, society needs to focus on one very important parameter. It is the cost to reduce CO_2 by one metric ton for each decarbonization activity ($/mtCO_2$). Activities include constructing new solar farms, wind farms and hydroelectric dams. These typically cost less than $50 per metric ton of CO_2 reduced (i.e. $\leq$ $50/mtCO_2$).

Most decarbonization initiatives do not decarbonize at lowest cost. Instead, they typically serve the interests of various groups, such as labor unions or the automobile industry. This is often overlooked, primarily because $/mtCO_2$ data for each initiative is not well documented. Alternatively, if unbiased government engineers scored each program for $/mtCO_2$, decarbonizing at lowest cost would be more likely.

The Green Line does not Occur Unless Required

If a consumer has a choice between buying a product that emits CO_2, and one that does not, they often ignore CO_2 and select the lower cost option. Many people consider their own CO_2 to be insignificant, and prefer the world's other inhabitants buy green and pay more. This is observed behavior, and is consistent with economic theory. Subsequently, to do the Green Line, decarbonization would need to be required by law. For an example of required decarbonization, one can look at California. They *require* 3% of their carbon-based electricity to be replaced with green electricity each year.

The Power Company

Power companies typically reduce the most CO_2 at relatively little cost. And everyone else typically reduces little CO_2 at relatively high costs. Everyone else is typically driven by labor union interests, automobile industry interests, green marketing, carbon offset scams, and news reports that ignore decarbonization cost (e.g. $/mtCO_2$). Below are several examples:

- When one switches from a gas vehicle to an electric vehicle, decarbonization costs are typically in excess of $220/mtCO_2$.
- The cost of electricity from residential solar is typically 3-times more than the cost of electricity from solar farms. This is due to the overhead associated with each residential project that causes costs to exceed $200/mtCO_2$.

Carbon Offsets

Many companies want to report they emit little or no CO_2. To do this, they pay organizations to supposedly reduce CO_2 emissions, to offset their own emissions. These are referred to as "carbon offsets", and they often sell for $3 to $5 per ton of CO_2 reduced.

Unfortunately, there are many offset schemes that are economically invalid, scientifically invalid, or fraudulent. For example, if someone is paid to not do tree farming on one parcel of land, to supposedly reduce CO_2, it will be done elsewhere. This is due to lumber production being set by demand. In other words, if one parcel of land is blocked, the home builder will get his 2x4 boards from a different parcel of land.

Some carbon offset schemes supposedly reduce CO_2 by planting trees. However, this only works if the trees and their offspring persists for thousands of years at no additional cost, which is often unlikely.

Capital needs to flow to where it is needed most. Therefore, government should consider shutting down schemes with inaccurate claims.

Corporate Social Responsibility

Some companies buy carbon offsets that match their CO_2 emissions. This is referred to as "net zero," and it is often done to appear more socially responsible. Also, these companies must decide if they want to pay more, and be at real net zero, or pay less and be at less than net zero. For example, a company that emits 10 million tons of CO_2 each year could buy $15-per-ton *real* offsets for $150M, or $3-per-ton *fraudulent* offsets for $30M. In both cases, they report net zero. However, in the latter case, their profit is $120M higher.

Some companies use their market position to block competitors and increase revenue; and this makes net zero more affordable. For example, Apple, Google, and Microsoft all sell proprietary operating systems from which it is difficult for their customers to migrate. This causes profit to be relatively high, and causes net zero to be more affordable. However, energy intensive companies, companies that compete on price, and publicly traded companies often cannot afford real net zero.

Publicly traded companies are required to report financial performance every three months, and if profit is slightly below market expectations, their share price decreases. Therefore, they often cannot afford additional expenses. However, if shareholders agree to an additional expense ahead of time, and it is included in market expectations, they can sometimes justify it.

Automated Decarbonization

Automated systems are needed to decarbonize for real, without fraud, at large scales, and at less than $50-per-ton of CO_2. To eliminate fraud, these would need to be heavily monitored and regulated by government. For details on how this might work, see the "The National Solar Farm" chapter.

Change the Climate with a Website

It took many weeks for the EIA to update their models and calculate the expected impact of the U.S. Inflation Reduction Act of 2022. And this occurred *after* the IRA was passed. In other words, lawmakers made decisions without knowing the impact of policy options. Operating blindly puts one at risk of ineffective policy and wasted money.

Lawmakers need better tools to guide them through decarbonization. And not just a little better. Much better. More specifically, websites are needed that calculate the cost and impact of various decarbonization initiatives. These would help lawmakers make decisions, help journalists understand decarbonization economics, and help voters better understand costs.

Doing this correctly might require hundreds of engineers, scientists, and economists that develop databases, models, and simulations. For details, see the "Fight Carbon with Websites" chapter.

Fuel Price Collapse

Decarbonization by definition involves less consumption of national gas, oil and coal. Less consumption leads to excess supply, which leads to lower fuel price. And this entails less money for fossil fuel companies. They do not want to downsize. Therefore, they pay lobbyists and make political donations to oppose decarbonization.

You Cannot Do the Green Line without Fuel Price Collapse

You cannot do the Green Line without carbon fuel price collapse. And it is not clear how many lawmakers would accept large declining companies in their districts. In other words, do not expect all lawmakers who supported Mild Decarbonization in the past, to support the Green Line.

Carbon Producers are not likely to Support the Green Line

Regions that produce fossil fuels are not likely to support the Green Line due to the social and economic pain it would bring to some of their employers. Fortunately, most regions do not produce fossil fuels. For example, only 36% of the states in the U.S. produce either natural gas or coal. The other states import these fuels and therefore benefit from the Green Line since it entails adding green jobs locally, and it entails paying less when fuel prices decrease due to less fuel consumption.

The Green Line Requires Support from Green Republicans

Republicans concerned about climate change are sometimes referred to as "Green Republicans". And according to survey, 40% of Republicans are Green. However, not one U.S. Republican Senator voted for the IRA due to its many provisions that do not decarbonize at lowest cost.

Approximately 37% of U.S. Senators are *Democrats* from states that do not produce natural gas or coal. This is not a majority. Therefore, the Green Line probably requires support from Green Republicans.

The Current Climate Coalition Has Only Produced Mild Decarbonization

Proponents of decarbonization have not had the political strength to fight the oil, coal and natural gas industries by themselves. Therefore, they formed a coalition with labor unions and the automobile industry, and provided them with protectionism in return for their support. This resulted in Mild Decarbonization, and resulted in programs that often cost more than $50/mtCO_2$.

The Green Line Needs a Different Coalition

To do the Green Line, one would probably need a coalition of Green Republicans and Democrats from the 64% of states that do not produce natural gas and do not produce coal. To engage Green Republicans, the Democrats might ask them "How do you want to decarbonize?" The only thing Democrats would need to do is require a plan that government engineers at EIA score as reducing CO_2 by approximately 170M metric tons each year. In other words, "Do the Green Line."

Figure 5.1: Washington, DC capital building.

6. Who Blocks Decarbonization in the U.S.?

The fossil fuel industries, and their suppliers, support many people. However, they are not a majority and the majority want to decarbonize according to surveys. Ultimately, we are looking at a political fight between "Carbon" and "Climate". They are both in an existential crisis. They are both fighting for their lives.

The primary participants on the climate battlefield are as follows.

Climate: People concerned about climate change.
Carbon: Fossil fuel industries and their suppliers.
Labor: Labor unions and their workers.
Green Republicans: Republicans who want to decarbonize.

U.S. Climate Politics

National media often portrays the climate war as a fight between those who want to decarbonize and those who do not. However, this is an oversimplification. The truth is more nuanced and is summarized as follows.

- Carbon spends significantly more money on lobbying, and makes more political donations than Climate. The Sierra Club and their friends are small relative to an industry.

- An industry's political activity is backed by a profit model. In other words, they spend one dollar on lobbying and political donations, and get back more than one dollar in benefit. Climate's model is different. Their benefit is to someone else, far into the future. And they are not supported by an industry's revenue stream.

- Climate is not politically strong enough to fight Carbon by themselves. Therefore, they typically elicit help from Labor, who requires protectionism in return for their support. This leads to provisions that favor U.S. manufacturers over lower cost imports. Ironically, these increase CO_2 emissions when they increase decarbonization costs.

- According to a survey, 60% of Republican voters do not want to decarbonize. Therefore, Green Republican lawmakers cannot be too vocal about their views. And they are a small group relative to the Democrats. Consequently, they often go unnoticed.

- Republicans are not opposed to green electricity. For example, red states North Carolina (47%) and Arizona (45%) each produce more green electricity as a percentage of total than blue states Florida (16%), Nevada (23%), and Massachusetts (29%). The values in parenthesis refer to the percentage of electricity in each state that is generated without emitting CO_2.

- Politically liberal coalitions have formed most climate legislation. Subsequently, it contains many fiscally liberal provisions, and these are not accepted by fiscally conservative Republicans. For example, Green Republicans often do not support decarbonization measures that cost more than $50/mtCO$_2$.

- Lawmakers from regions that produce coal or natural gas are not likely to support the Green Line due to the social and economic pain it would bring to many of their employers.

- Approximately two-thirds of the U.S. states do not produce natural gas and do not produce coal. Instead, they import fuel, and they benefit from low fuel prices. A coalition of Democrats and Green Republicans from these states could potentially decarbonize electricity at less than $50/mtCO$_2$.

- Republicans and Democrats often do not get along. However, simple legislation is sometimes possible when they begin with a common goal, and give each other veto power over each provision.

Carbon Blocks Decarbonization with Money

The five largest petroleum companies together spend $200M each year on lobbying to block decarbonization. Green organizations, like the Sierra Club, do not have this kind of money. And non-green Republicans who vote against climate remedies, for a variety of reasons, do not spend money to block Climate.

What does $200M buy? <u>Carbon wants Climate to believe</u> they are decarbonizing when they are not, to get them to fight less. To do this, some climate remedies are enacted; however, they are watered down relative to what is needed. In the end, decarbonization is mild.

Figure 6.1: A portion of an oil refinery's vast revenue is often used to protect their political interests.

Climate is a Small Monkey

Industries are politically powerful due to their vast wealth and large numbers of employees. Employees and their friends vote, while employees and their employers make political donations. To connect the dots, lobbyists suggest to lawmakers that donations and votes are contingent on support for specific measures.

Each industry is a political gorilla, while other groups metaphorically are small monkeys. The fossil fuel industry ("Carbon"), labor unions ("Labor"), automobile manufacturers ("Auto"), and groups of factories ("Manufacturing") are examples of political  gorillas. And a group of non-profits that encourage decarbonization ("Climate") is the small monkey.

In theory, a monkey can jump on a gorilla's back and ride forward. However, in practice, the gorilla typically receives most of the benefit, while the monkey gets the crumbs.

The Alliance between Climate and Labor

To get IRA to pass, Climate put together an alliance with Labor. For this reason, much of the IRA helps Labor and ignores CO_2. For example, one provision cancels the $7.5K subsidy on electric vehicles made outside North America. Ironically, this *increases* CO_2 emissions since it blocks low cost EVs from entering the U.S.

Cheap Green Car

One can buy a small EV in China with a 250-mile range for $17K, an example of which is pictured below. If these were allowed into the U.S. with a $7K subsidy, final price would be $10K. And this would cause more families with two cars to consider having one gas muscle car and one light electric. Normally, Americans favor more car for more money. However, a $10K price would cause some to reconsider.

Figure 6.2: EV Dolphin (Atto 2) manufactured by China's BYD in 2021.

Protectionism

Many nations protect their domestic manufacturers from foreign-made goods. They do this with import tariffs, government subsidies for domestically manufactured goods, and regulations that block imports. These practices are commonly referred to as "protectionism". They reduce trade deficits, help domestic manufacturers, and help domestic Labor.

However, they also increase prices, increase inflation, hurt domestic consumers, and do not reduce CO_2.

The U.S. implemented little protectionism over the last several decades, and this made it easier for Americans to shop. However, the Trump administration increased protectionism with more import tariffs, and the Biden administration increased it with legislation like the IRA.

Protectionism is a form of trade warfare where a nation demands more access to foreign markets, in return for increased access to one's own markets. In other words, nations occasionally agree to protect less with respect to each other.

Arrangements are codified in what are called Free Trade Agreements (FTA). As of 2022, the U.S. had FTA arrangements with 20 countries. This included Canada, Mexico, Korea, and Australia. However, it did not include China, Japan, India, and European countries.

Figure 6.3: Ships often carry hundreds of millions of dollars' worth of cargo, which effectively transfers wealth from one country to another.

The Chinese block many imports into China with regulations. And they often copy products designed by others. This drives the Americans crazy. In response, the IRA links electric vehicle subsidies to these practices. For example, EVs made with Chinese battery components will not receive U.S.

government subsidies, unless the Chinese soften their business practices, which is unlikely.

Figure 6.4: Trade relations between the United States and China are often tense.

The Easiest Way to Decarbonize Transportation

The easiest way to decarbonize U.S. transportation is to pick on a different industry to protect. However, this is not likely since Climate's political power is small relative to the combined strength of Carbon, Labor and Auto. If we use the monkey analogy, this would be like one small monkey overpowering several gorillas.

Figure 6.5: Industrial robots assemble automobiles at low-cost.

7.   The Existential Crisis of Carbon

To better understand what is happening, one needs to take a break from Climate and explore Carbon.

The Pain of Decarbonization

Decarbonization, by definition, would have a devastating impact on the fossil fuel industries, and their suppliers.

We are looking at replacing coal, natural gas and oil with green energy. And less consumption of carbon-based fuels would lead to excess fuel supply, which would lead to lower fuel prices. The combination of less quantity and less revenue-per-unit would have a devastating impact on the entire fuel supply chain. This includes exploration, extraction, refining, storage and distribution. In other words, decarbonization would cause companies involved in carbon, and their suppliers, to downsize.

Even the threat of fuel price collapse is enough to cause carbon companies to shudder. This is because they have lived it. They have lived through periods of low fuel prices and high. And they know low entails significantly less money in their pockets.

Also, if government enacted significant decarbonization legislation, Carbon's ability to borrow money would decrease immediately. For example, banks would reduce loans to build offshore drilling platforms, fearing those loans would not be repaid. And banks instead would lend to builders of solar farms and wind farms since long term demand for their product would be more likely.

Transferable Carbon Skills

If a petroleum company were a broadly defined energy company instead of a narrowly defined petroleum company, they might be able to maintain their revenue while the world moves from carbon. However, in most cases, petroleum companies do not have the equipment and expertise to compete against solar and land-based wind farm construction companies.

Petroleum companies have some transferable skills. For example, carbon, capture and sequestration (CCS) is similar to natural gas extraction, processing and distribution. And offshore windmills are slightly similar to offshore drilling platforms and their associated underwater infrastructure. However, CCS and offshore windmills are costly relative to other decarbonization options, and are therefore in less demand.

Some laid-off oil workers might find themselves working at a wind farm, closer to home, and with better pay. However, many carbon workers would not see better jobs.

Our Changing World

Let's take a break from Carbon and talk about manufacturing.

Boston Dynamics recently demonstrated robots with dance moves more complex than the repetitive tasks performed by most factory workers. These robots are currently manufactured in low volumes and at high costs. However, their costs would be less if they were mass produced.

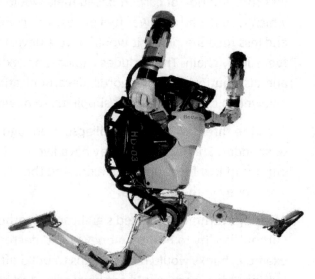

Imagine a $2K robot that operates for 5 years, works 160 hours a week, moves 3 times faster than a human, and has cameras that inspect more accurately. Now, compare this with a human factory worker making $10K a year. It will soon cost 10 to 100-times less to assemble by robot than human.

It was painful for many U.S. factory workers when they were replaced by international workers several decades ago. And it will be painful for many international workers when robots eventually replace them.

Our world is constantly changing. And this results in crisis for some, and opportunity for others. Energy is changing too, and its transformation will probably be as seismic as that experienced by manufacturing.

8.   Fight Carbon with Websites

Carbon's strategy is to throw Climate activists "red meat". In other words, have ineffective decarbonization legislation pass so that Climate fights less. This only works if journalists and lawmakers fail to understand the costs and impact of proposed legislation. Unfortunately, this is exactly what happens due to the fact it is not well documented. This might seem absurd, because it is. However, this can be fixed, as we discuss in this chapter.

Where Do Decarbonizers Go for Good Information?

To calculate the effect of U.S. decarbonization legislation, one would need help from U.S. government scientists, engineers and economists. These mostly reside at the U.S. Energy Information Administration (EIA) and at the U.S. National Renewable Energy Laboratory (NREL). In theory, U.S. lawmakers can request a graph that shows projected U.S. CO_2 emissions, with and without a government initiative. The difference between the two is the effect of the initiative. A theoretical example is shown below.

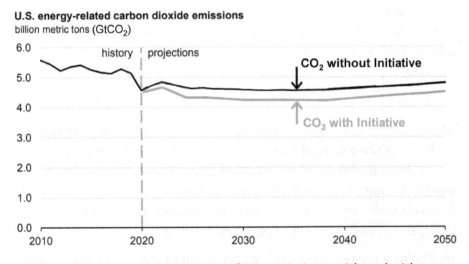

Figure 8.1: Conceptual projection of CO_2 emissions, with and without a decarbonization initiative.

The *difference* between the two plots is the amount of CO_2 reduced each year due to the initiative (e.g. $GtCO_2$/yr). And one can divide this difference by the cost of the initiative ($/yr) to calculate the cost to reduce emissions by one ton of CO_2 ($/mtCO_2$). Also, one can divide cost ($/yr) by population to calculate cost-per-person-per-year ($/person/yr).

In theory, one can calculate cost and impact of many different initiatives. For example, "What happens when 5% of electricity is required to decarbonize each year?" Or 3% each year? In theory, multiple reports could identify how to get to zero at lowest cost.

Change the Climate with a Website

A website could potentially analyze different policies in different countries. For example, it could look at what happens when electricity is required to decarbonize at X percent-per-year at lowest cost, over Y years, in country Z. Anyone with a web browser could then specify X, Y, and Z and instantly see cost and impact.

The website could also support individual states and metropolitan areas. For example, state and city officials might want to see the cost and impact of different amounts of required decarbonization.

Calculation models already exist. For example, the U.S. government has a model called "NEMS", and it can be <u>downloaded</u> for free. However, website user interface, support for user input, support for different regions is lacking.

Trust is Required

Many models are not trusted and are subsequently ignored. However, much can be done to elicit trust. This includes: (a) building on top of existing models that are already trusted by government, (b) collaborating with government engineers, (c) requiring materials be made open source, (d) paying scientists to review models, (e) requiring reviews be made public, and (f) paying others to copy and improve.

Developing a trusted system might cost 10-times more than developing an ignored system.

Some Regions Make Money by Decarbonizing

Modeling different cities and regions is important since some make money by decarbonizing, and these need to be identified. For example, pipes that carry natural gas into the city of Boston, MA, USA are too small. And this has created a regional natural gas shortage, which has increased the price of natural gas and electricity. If Boston decarbonized electricity, the local price of natural gas and electricity would probably decrease.

States that import carbon-based fuels would probably benefit from lower fuel prices, and are therefore more inclined to support the Green Line. The same is true with nations that import fuel. For this reason, it would be helpful to have a website that identifies cities, regions and nations that benefit from decarbonization. These would then be more inclined to decarbonize locally, and to form coalitions that favor doing the Green Line.

Planet Saving Website

Below is an illustration of a website that calculates the cost and impact of a user defined decarbonization strategy. This is not a real website, only a concept.

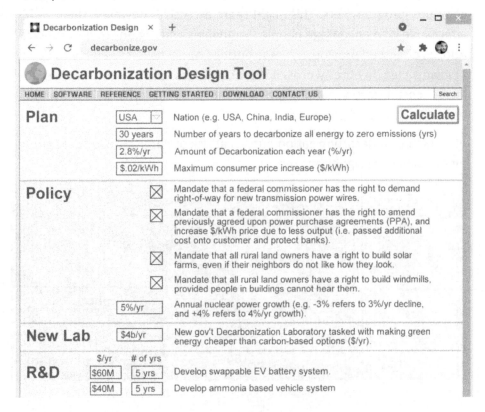

Figure 8.2: Conceptual illustration of website that calculates impact of decarbonization policy.

One might begin by modeling green electricity subsidies (e.g. subsidize green electricity by X ¢/kWh) and green electricity requirements (e.g. electricity is required to decarbonize at Y %/yr). And calculate cost of initiative, cost-per-person, CO_2 reduced, decarbonization cost ($/mtCO_2$), natural gas price, coal price, savings-per-person due to cheaper fuel, savings-per-person due to cheaper food, number of carbon jobs-lost, number of green jobs-added, and locations of lost and added jobs.

The Green Line would be more feasible if voters had a better sense of cost-per-person and lawmakers had a better sense of how jobs-gained offset jobs-lost. Or in the case of regions that import fuel, how job-gained are local, and jobs-lost are elsewhere.

Creating databases, models, and simulations for many regions and many policy options would require hundreds or thousands of engineers and computer programmers. This might seem excessive. However, the alternative is to encourage people, companies and regions to decarbonize. And, as discussed previously, these entities rarely have the ability to do so at lowest cost. In other words, it is probably less costly to accurately model lowest-cost decarbonization, and have these models drive policy, than to operate blindly and pay more.

Also, high-cost decarbonization puts us at risk of paralysis due to fatigue, before achieving significant results.

9.   Fight Carbon with Wealth

Many wealthy individuals and foundations have expressed an interest in using money to save the planet. However, what, where, and how to spend is often unclear. This chapter offers a few suggestions.

Build Planet Saving Website ($10M to $100M)

If one is looking to save the planet for $10M to $100M, consider building the website discussed in the previous chapter. To get started, one might send the following kind of email to U.S. government engineers who are already modeling energy and emissions:

> Dear AnnualEnergyOutlook (at) eia.gov,
>
> I would like to create a NEMS-like website that calculates the cost and impact of various decarbonization policies. I am willing to supply the money if your office is willing to help oversee the project in some way.

Someone like Michael Bloomberg would be uniquely suited for this since he has a background in modeling markets, and he has a foundation that fights Carbon.

Publish Planet Saving Book ($100K to $3M)

If one wants to spend several million dollars to save the planet, consider hiring a university to improve this book. For example, MIT professors could potentially publish "MIT's Plan to Save the Planet". To get started, one might send the following kind of email to the university of their choosing:

> Dear Dean of Engineering,
>
> I would like to spend $X of my own money to develop a plan to reduce CO_2 emissions to zero. For an example of an existing open-source plan writing project, see "www.APlanToSaveThePlanet.org"...

Venture capitalist John Doerr would be uniquely suited for this since he is familiar with plan writing and he has already written a book on climate change.

Set up Decarbonization Laboratory ($100M to $10B)

For larger money, one could potentially set up a decarbonization laboratory, as discussed in the "National Decarbonization Laboratory" chapter. A laboratory could have almost any number of divisions, and almost any number of groups within each division. And one could add or subtract at any time. Also, each division and each group could potentially be funded to almost any level.

A new laboratory would need a business plan. And to get started, one could potentially copy and modify any of the chapters in this book at no charge.

Bill Gates and Elon Musk would be uniquely suited for this since they both have a history of R&D leadership, and they both have an interest in climate change.

If their staff wanted guidance, their leader could potentially add notes next to areas of interest within this book.

Write Decarbonization Laboratory Business Plan ($100K to $1M)

For $100K to $1M one could potentially hire a university to write a business plan for a decarbonization laboratory. The university might prefer to own the plan after writing. However, if required to publish open source, others could more easily make use of it.

Conclusion

Many wealthy individuals have expressed an interest in saving the planet. However, figuring out how to spend wisely is not easy. Hopefully, some of the ideas in this book will help them venture forward.

10. Fight Carbon with Regions that Import Coal and Natural Gas

We will now discuss how some regions benefit from decarbonization. This is important, since they are the ones that are likely to push the Green Line forward. Before we begin, we will review how to decarbonize all sources of CO_2 at lowest cost. Decarbonization activity can be divided into three broad areas:

- **Electricity:** Generate electricity with solar farms, wind farms, hydroelectric dams and nuclear power plants; instead of generating electricity by burning coal or natural gas.

- **Transportation:** Power vehicles with green electricity, green hydrogen, or green ammonia; instead of gasoline or diesel fuel.

- **Heat:** Make heat in buildings and factories with green electricity or green hydrogen; instead of burning natural gas or coal.

Decarbonizing electricity tends to cost little, whereas decarbonizing transportation and decarbonizing heat tend to be expensive. Therefore, if one wants to reduce $1/30^{th}$ of emissions each year at lowest cost, they might first focus on electricity *while* reducing the cost of transportation and heat decarbonization via R&D.

Fight Carbon with Lower Fuel Prices

In some cases, decarbonizing electricity can save consumers money even if the green electricity initially cost a little more than the carbon-based electricity.

The price of carbon-based electricity is largely determined by the price of natural gas and coal fuel. And fuel prices often decrease when fuel consumption decreases.

Let's look at an example to see how this might work. Let's assume a region starts out by generating 100% of its electricity with 3¢ (per kWh) natural gas, and 20% is replaced with 4¢ green electricity. Let's also assume that less natural gas consumption leads to price decreasing from 3¢ to 2¢. The resulting blended electricity ends up costing 2.4¢, which is less than the original 3¢ ((20% x 4¢) + (80% x 2¢)). In other words, in some cases, one can save money when moving to greener electricity.

Fight Carbon with Regions that Import Coal

Coal is produced in a relatively small region within the U.S., as shown below in light blue.

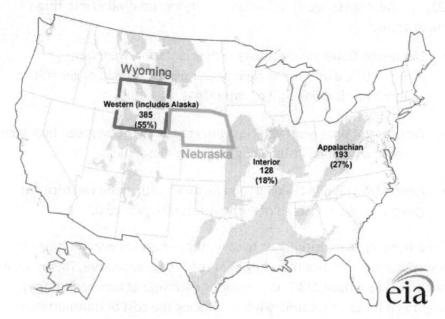

Figure 10.1: Sources of coal in the U.S.

Coal employs about 50K people in the U.S. and therefore has political power at the federal level, and at the local level within regions that produce it. However, coal does not have political power at the local level in non-producing regions (shown above in white). Subsequently, non-producers who consume coal *benefit* from a lower coal price. They also gain jobs if they replace coal-based electricity with local green jobs. In other words, in many regions, decarbonizing coal results in green jobs being added locally while carbon jobs are lost elsewhere. And coal *importers* do not fear coal price collapse since it allows them to save money.

Wyoming, shown above in red, is an example of a coal exporter and neighboring Nebraska, show above in green, is an example of a coal importer. Wyoming employs 5K coal workers and Nebraska employs none. Therefore, Nebraska might be inclined to support decarbonizing coal, while Wyoming opposes it.

One can apply this logic to entire countries that import coal.

A website is needed that identifies cities, regions, and entire nations that save money and create local jobs when coal-based electricity is replaced with green electricity.

Fight Carbon with Regions that Import Natural Gas

One can apply the same logic to natural gas. Regions that import natural gas can potentially benefit from replacing natural gas-based electricity with green electricity. The map below shows reserves of natural gas in the U.S. As one can see, many regions are importers of natural gas.

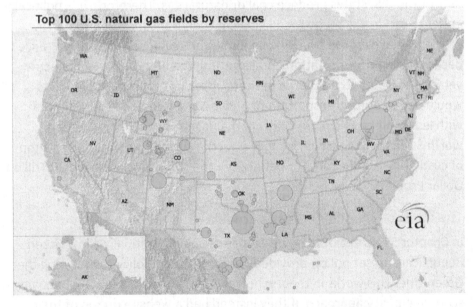

Figure 10.2: Locations of natural gas in the U.S.

U.S. Energy Politics

The U.S. produces approximately 1 trillion cubic meters of natural gas each year. This comes from approximately 25% of the states. This includes AK, AR, CO, LA, NM, ND, OH, OK, PA, TX, WV, and WY.

The U.S. also produces approximately 0.7 billion tons of coal each year. This also comes from approximately 25% of the states. This includes AL, CO, IL, IN, KY, ND, PA, TX, UT, VA, WV, and WY.

The following states control approximately two-thirds of the U.S. congress and they do *not* produce coal and do *not* produce natural gas: AZ, CA, CT, DE, FL, GA, HI, ID, IA, KS, ME, MD, MA, MI, MN, MS, MO, MT, NE, NV, NH, NJ, NY, NC, OR, RI, SC, SD, TN, VT, WA, and WI.

Do not Fight Oil while Fighting Coal and Natural Gas

If legislation focuses exclusively on decarbonizing electricity, it only needs to contend with natural gas and coal interests. And if it adds transportation, it also needs to contend with oil interests. Approximately 50% of the U.S. states produce oil, coal, or natural gas. And approximately 36% of the U.S. states produce coal or natural gas. Therefore, it is politically easier to tackle electricity today, and chew on transportation tomorrow. Also, this makes sense from an economic and technical perspective, since decarbonizing transportation entails getting the lifetime costs of electric vehicles to be less than that of gas cars. After this is achieved, markets would decarbonize transportation. And lower EV costs can be achieved with less protectionism, or a battery that lasts twice as long. Both are worth $10K to $20K, which is more than the current $7.5K subsidy on top of costly U.S. production. For details, see the "Transportation is a 30 Trillion Dollar Problem" chapter.

The Climate Monkey's Secret Power

In Chapter 5, we explored how Democrats could potentially allow Green Republicans to set policy, provided EIA scores their policy as following the Green Line. This works in theory; however, it takes EIA weeks to manually score one policy approach. If they instead had a website on top of their model, lawmakers could more easily identify a path forward.

If the little Climate monkey is looking for a secret power to help fight the Carbon gorilla; it is probably a website that identifies cities, regions and nations throughout the world that can save money and create local jobs while reducing CO_2. This website could also identify coalitions of fuel importers who could work together to reduce fuel costs via less fuel consumption, while adding local green jobs.

11. Fight Carbon with Better Alliances

The U.S. government passed the Inflation Reduction Act (IRA) in August of 2022, and several of its provisions reduce CO_2. The centerpiece entails a seven year extension of the 1¢/kWh green electricity subsidy. This is implemented with tax credits that use government money to reduce the effective price of green electricity. This subsidy had been in place since 2006 and was scheduled to end in 2025. However, the IRA extended it to 2032, and also gave the U.S. Secretary of Energy the authority to extend it further to 2050. The IRA's extension does not affect today's green electricity, or green electricity from facilities built before 2026. However, it will reduce the effective cost of green electricity from facilities built after 2025.

The below Feb 2022 graph from EIA shows the number of solar farms and wind farms that are expected to be built each year over the next 30 years. This graph was published before the IRA was passed, and therefore does not reflect its impact. The height of each bar above the zero line reflects the amount of power generation built each year. Solar farms are shown in yellow, wind farms are shown in green, and natural gas-based power plants are shown in light blue.

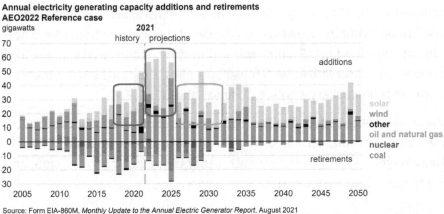

Figure 11.1: Projection of U.S. solar farm and wind farm construction each year over the next 30 years.

The above graph shows solar farm and wind farm construction decreasing after 2025 due to the expected expiration of the 1¢/kWh subsidy (i.e. the area circled in green is less than the area circled in red). However, with the IRA's extension, this 2025 decrease is instead expected to occur sometime between 2032 and 2050.

The graph also shows green electricity construction *increasing* around 2021 (i.e. the area circled in red is larger than the area circled in blue). This was due to an increase in the cost of natural gas and coal fuel in 2021, and not from a subsidy increase. This fuel price increase made green electricity more affordable relative to carbon-based electricity. In many cases, fuel prices have a greater impact than subsidies, as discussed in later chapters.

As noted previously, the U.S. decarbonized electricity at 0.5% per year between 2017 and 2021, and the 1¢/kWh green electricity subsidy was in place during that time. This decarbonization rate is lower than what is needed; therefore, do not expect this subsidy by itself to solve the climate problem.

Can the Inflation Reduction Act be Improved?

If the entire 700 page IRA was replaced with the following sentence, more CO_2 would be reduced: *U.S. electricity is required to decarbonize at 6% each year over 9 years, at lowest cost.*

To improve the IRA, one might elicit help from fiscal conservatives who want to decarbonize. However, unlike Labor, fiscal conservatives are not fond of subsidies for U.S. companies. Therefore, if one gains support from some fiscal conservatives with fewer subsidies, they might lose support from other lawmakers who are close to Labor.

If subsidies were reduced to the extent required by Green Republicans, and the number of solar farm and wind farm workers were increased, then Labor might stay engaged. However, Labor is not looking for any job, or many jobs. They are looking for well-paying jobs.

Consider Buying Labor

In theory, one could increase wages at solar farms and wind farms in return for Labor's support of the Green Line. This could be done by several techniques, such as requiring workers be paid a prevailing wage.

Let's run the numbers to see how much this might cost the typical homeowner. Let's assume each house consumes 10,000 kWh of electricity each year, 30% comes from solar farms, solar operations cost 1¢/kWh, 40% of this is labor, and worker compensation is increased 50% to get Labor's support. According to the math, this would cost the homeowner $6 per year (10,000 x 30% x 1¢ x 40% x 50%).

Labor Should Welcome Decarbonization

The IRA tries to soften the blow from declining oil jobs by creating new green jobs. It does this with subsidizes to U.S. factories that make solar panels and EV batteries. However, making solar panels in the U.S. instead of China does not reduce CO_2. Instead, government money would be more effective if it created jobs by increasing the number of solar farms and wind farms constructed each year. Workers are needed to build and maintain these facilities, and to build supporting power transmission lines.

To decarbonize at lowest cost *and* meet the satisfaction of Labor, architects of climate legislation need to: (a) identify lowest-cost decarbonization projects (i.e. low $/mtCO_2$), and (b) make sure new jobs receive a prevailing wage. To help with this, a website is needed that calculates job-gained and wages given different policy options. In other words, to keep Labor engaged, we need detailed reports on new jobs.

If it is Not Working for Both Sides, it is Not Working

There is a saying in politics, "If it is not working for both sides, it is not working". And this probably applies to Green Republicans and Democrats with climate change. Both want to decarbonize. However, if one tries to decarbonize without the other's support, provisions are likely to be watered down, and implementation is likely to be impeded. In other words, it is probably in both sides best interest to provide the opposing side with veto power over each provision, to gain their support. And trust EIA to accurately score each policy approach.

If both sides could agree on a few sentences, then government engineers could take it from there. For an example of what those sentences might look like, see the beginning of the "Decarbonization Act of 202x" chapter.

Decarbonizing the Easiest, Laziest, and Cheapest Way Possible

The easiest way to decarbonize the U.S. is probably to: (a) require increasing amounts of green electricity, (b) have consumers pay the additional cost, (c) let power company engineers get it done at lowest cost, (d) reduce subsidies to garner support from Green Republicans, (e) buy Labor, and (f) work with a coalition of lawmakers from regions that import carbon-based fuels.

Perhaps the Little Climate Monkey needs a New Girl?

As we discussed previously, the Climate Monkey has been dating the Labor Gorilla for several years now. And it is possible she is not good for him. Perhaps he would be better off with a new girl, such as the Green Republicans? Perhaps she would let him have that cheap EV from China he has always wanted? Or perhaps he could date *both* Labor and Green Republicans, and keep them both calm with treats?

In either case, the possibility of fuel price collapse will cause their Carbon Gorilla friend to go bananas.

In summary, resolving climate change is a tricky political puzzle.

12. Fight Carbon with Food

A homeowner might compare the cost of decarbonization with the cost of a warmer planet, and only be inclined to decarbonize if the warm planet cost more.

Electricity Decarbonization cost-per-house

Already 40% of U.S. electricity is made without emitting CO_2. And if this increased to 100% using green electricity that cost 2¢/kWh more, the additional cost per house would be $120 each year (2¢ x 60% x 10,000 kWh/house/yr). This assumes the price of carbon fuel remains unchanged.

Climate's First Harm

Now let's look which warm planet cost first exceeds $120/year/house. One might think of this as *climate's first harm*. It is probably not sea level rise since that is expected later. And it is probably not more severe storms, since the odds of one's house being hit by a costly storm are low. We are already observing less water in rivers and reservoirs, in part due to climate change. And food prices are up, in part due to less water. Therefore, higher food costs might be climate's first harm. The canary in the climate coal mine.

Fight Carbon with Food

Warmer air leads to dryer land, dryer land leads to less food, and less food leads to higher food prices. And as mentioned previously, requiring decarbonization typically leads to higher electricity prices, at least initially.

In theory, a website could compare additional initial electricity costs, with additional food cost, in a dryer world. And it could identify ways to spend money today to reduce food costs tomorrow.

Let's look at an example to see how this might work. The average U.S. house spends $5,200 each year at the supermarket and if this increased by 20% due to dryer land, for example, additional cost would be $1,040 ($5,200 x 20%). Obviously, this is significantly more than the $120 per house to decarbonize electricity.

Connect Food to Climate

To better connect food to climate, foundations and governments could support websites that model decarbonization costs and warm planet costs. Or promote the concept of warm planet costs to the public. For example, they could sell promotional T-shirts at Amazon.com for $1, an example of which is pictured below.

Figure 12.1: Example promotional article that connects food costs to climate change costs. This is not an actual product.

Modeling Challenges

We sometimes see less water in rivers and reservoirs; however, this is not always due to climate change. For example, an increase in upstream agricultural production will likely lead to less water downstream. And more upstream farming could be caused by a variety of things, such as population growth. In other words, it is difficult to calculate how much climate change affects food prices. And if calculations are not done in an unbiased manner, they are likely to be ignored. To elicit trust, one can do a variety of things, as discussed in the "Fight Carbon with Websites" chapter.

13. Everyone's CO$_2$ Is Your CO$_2$

We will now explore how one might economically justify spending their money to reduce someone else's CO$_2$.

A Rising Sea Hits Landfill First

Much of Boston, Massachusetts, USA, was permanently covered by water in 1630. Then, over hundreds of years, it was filled in by engineers who added only enough material to meet their needs, as illustrated below left in light green. Also, according to the U.S. National Oceanic and Atmospheric Administration (NOAA), the sea will be 1.6m (5ft) higher 65 to 200 years from now. And this will cover Boston's landfill, as illustrated below right in light blue.

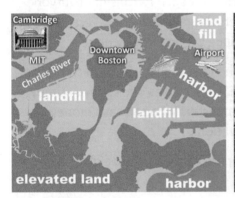 

Figure 13.1: Locations of the land-fill in Boston, MA, USA.

For details on other U.S. cities, visit NOAA's Sea Level Rise Viewer and enter an address at the top, and a sea level increase at the lower-left.

One might consider building a seawall, perhaps similar to the one in the movie *Blade Runner 2049*. However, a rising underground water table would eventually cause water to seep into basements and below-ground infrastructure, even if a seawall were in place.

Decarbonize Others to Help Yourself

The state of Massachusetts (MA) emits 1/500th of the world's CO$_2$. Therefore, if MA reduced emissions to zero, the world's 499/500th would still harm MA with a rising sea.

MA can put money into R&D or brute-force decarbonization. An example of R&D would be to develop a website that identifies the lowest cost method for others to decarbonize and how to justify it economically. An example of brute-force decarbonization would be to place solar panels on the roof of the Boston Public Library.

If MA compares the amount of CO_2 reduced globally per dollar spent with each of these, building a trusted website would probably do better. In other words, if MA had a fixed budget to minimize sea level rise in Boston 200 years from now, using their brains might do more than their muscles.

Everyone's CO_2 Is Your CO_2

Currently, nations and regions within nations are looking at decreasing their own CO_2. An alternative approach is for each to consider everyone else's CO_2 to be their CO_2 since it affects them. Below are several ways governments and foundations can reduce CO_2 in faraway places.

- Build websites that: (a) calculate the lowest cost way to decarbonize, (b) identify cases where decarbonization causes one to save money, and (c) identify coalitions of fuel importers who can save money by lowering fuel prices via decarbonization.

- Sponsor R&D that requires developed technology to be given away for free to increase utilization.

- Build transparent factories that others can copy for free to reduce the manufacturing costs of green products.

The latter two suggestions help foreign manufacturers and, therefore, might not be popular with some lawmakers. However, if one looks at the amount of CO_2 reduced per dollar spent, they might find these appealing.

Several foundations have expressed an interest in spending billions of dollars to tackle climate change. They tend not to favor one nation over another. Therefore, they are in a unique position to fully maximize CO_2 reduction per R&D dollar. They can do this by: (a) tasking panels of the smartest and most experienced in the world with R&D objectives, (b) providing them with ample funding, (c) requiring produced materials to be open source, (d) monitoring money flow, and (e) adjusting as needed.

14. Climate Change Is a 100 Trillion Dollar Problem

Tackling climate change entails transitioning from a carbon-based economy to one that does not emit CO_2. This is referred to as "decarbonization," and it entails building new infrastructure that is likely to cost the world approximately 100 trillion dollars over several decades. Approximately one-third for electrical power generation, one-third for cars, and one-third for factories.

~$30T - Solar farms, wind farms, hydroelectric dams, more grid

~$30T - 1.5 billion cars x $20K per car

~$40T - New factories and agriculture that do not emit CO_2

How Much Energy Do We Need?

Each year the world produces <u>583</u> exajoules (EJ) of heat energy, and if this were fed into a 35% efficient turbine, 56,000 TWh/yr of electricity would be produced.

We know how much electricity is produced by large facilities like the Hoover dam in Nevada. Therefore, we can divide 56,000 TWh/yr by their production to calculate roughly how many <u>facilities</u> one would need to match global energy production.

Figure 14.1: Large sources of green electricity.

For example, 56,000 TWh/yr corresponds to 17,200 <u>Hoover Dams</u>, 22,700 <u>London Arrays</u>, 44,200 <u>Topaz Solar Farms</u>, and 22-times the <u>world's nuclear fission reactors</u>.

# of sites	TWh/yr	Site	Description
17,171	3.3	Hoover Dam	Large dam in Nevada
44,200	1.3	Topas Solar Farm	Solar farm in California
22,666	2.5	London Array	175 windmills in water, near London, UK
22	2,553	All Nuclear Reactor	Power generated by all fission reactors

Figure 14.2: Number of select facilities needed to replace the world's energy consumption.

The Topaz solar farm produces 0.55GW of electricity, and solar farms cost $1.12-per-watt at today's prices (NREL, 2022, CAPEX). Therefore 44,200 would cost 27 trillion dollars in total ($1.12 x 0.55GW x 44,200).

Topaz's panels sit on approximately 4 square miles, therefore 44,200 facilities would consume 176K square miles (44,200 x 4). The state of Texas is 268K square miles; therefore, this would fit nicely in 65% of Texas (176K / 268K).

Solar power is intermittent; therefore, coating Texas with solar would not be a direct replacement for carbon-based sources that are available 24x7. And we are combining consumers of heat with consumers of electricity, which differ in multiple ways. Also we are not taking into consideration GDP growth. In other words, this analysis is only an approximation. However, it does provide a rough idea of how much green energy construction is needed globally over several decades.

Easy at First and More Difficult Later

Initially, solar, wind, and hydro projects are built in the most favorable conditions. However, as one builds, conditions often become less favorable, and costs increase. Hydroelectric dams prefer sloped land with running water. Wind farms prefer windy land away from people or windy shallow water close to shore. And solar farms prefer cheap, cleared, sunny land not far from cities. In other words, decarbonization is likely to be easier at first and more difficult later.

Material Fabrication Needs to be Decarbonized Too

Thousands of solar farms, wind farms, and hydroelectric dams would consume significant amounts of metal and cement. Fabricating these materials with carbon-based fuels would cause CO_2 emissions to increase. Therefore, material fabrication needs to be decarbonized too. In theory, the lowest cost way to do this is with nuclear reactors in China. More about this later.

Can We Afford $100T?

Gross Domestic Product (GDP) worldwide is $96T per year. If we assume inflation and growth are zero, to simplify, GDP over 30 years would be $2,880T ($96T x 30yrs). Subsequently, $100T of infrastructure, built over 30 years, would consume 3.5% of GDP ($100T / $2,880T).

We are looking at bonds and bank loans paying for green infrastructure instead of it paying for carbon-based infrastructure. For example, we are looking at building wind farms in water, instead of building oil drilling platforms in water. Unfortunately, in many cases, green infrastructure costs more. For example, we need more windmills than oil drilling platforms.

Harm from a warmer planet is costly too. For example, damage from sea level rise, damage from storms, and damage from dryer land are all costly. Fortunately, the cost of decarbonization is less than that of a warmer planet. However, decarbonization costs are immediate, and many warmer planet costs are several decades away.

How Smart Are We?

In many cases, a population favors itself over its future self. Yet to what extent? As evidence of climate change increases, support for decarbonization also increases. According to a survey, 67% of Americans want to decarbonize. This suggests significant steps will be taken this decade.

However, will we be smart and decarbonize at the lowest cost?

Unfortunately, the answer is "no," due economic and political strategies that are fundamentally flawed, as discussed previously.

How Do We Spend Billions of Dollars to Save Trillions?

In theory, one can reduce the cost of green infrastructure with more R&D. Nevertheless, it is unclear what and where to develop. Subsequently, we should be asking top scientists and engineers the following question:

> *How might we spend additional hundreds of billions of dollars on R&D, over approximately a decade, to save trillions of dollars on green infrastructure?*

In conclusion, we need to think about climate change as a 100 trillion dollar problem and consider how to spend billions of dollars to save trillions.

15. The Failure of Climate Information

Our failure to act is partly due to published information that is either wrong or incomplete. Below are several examples.

Example #1: Electricity Vehicles

Approximately 2.8M EVs and Plug-in EVs were sold in the U.S. between 2010 and 2022. Each reduces CO_2 by approximately 3.6 tons a year; therefore, the total CO_2 reduction is 10 million tons each year (2.8M x 3.6t). The U.S. emits approximately 5 billion tons of CO_2 each year. Therefore, EV production over the last 12 years has only reduced it by 1/500th (10Mt / 5Gt).

The total cost of EV lifetime ownership has been thousands of dollars more than gas cars, partly due to replacement battery costs. If one divides this additional cost by the amount of CO_2 reduced, one can see hundreds of dollars for each ton of CO_2 avoided. This is much higher than many other decarbonization initiatives. For details, see the "Transportation is a 30 Trillion Dollar Problem" chapter.

Example #2: Green Electricity

According to NREL, U.S. electricity costs are ~3¢/kWh with solar farms and land-based wind farms, ~5¢/kWh with solar panels on commercial buildings, ~6¢/kWh with offshore wind farms, and ~9¢/kWh with solar panels on homes. In other words, some sources are cheap, and others are less so. These costs tend to decrease over time, but their ratios change little since the more costly sources are also more complicated.

Consumers rarely buy a product at a high price when they can get it for less. Therefore, higher-cost options are less likely to scale up appreciably.

Journalists Often Ignore Economics

Journalists seldom discuss how the cost of a remedy compares with the cost of alternatives. In other words, they often ignore economics. In some cases, they are unaware of the costs of the remedy or the costs of the alternatives.

Misdirection to Make Money

Groups and individuals sometimes provide incorrect or incomplete information to make money. This includes: (a) companies that sell products or services, (b) special interest groups with agendas, (c) professors who promote research to increase funding, (d) shareholders who talk the talk to increase the share price, and (e) entrepreneurs who raise capital. These biases sometimes affect reports in national media, published papers, websites, and books.

Where Does One Go for Good Information?

The U.S. Energy Information Administration (EIA) and the U.S. National Renewable Energy Laboratory (NREL) are tasked with providing unbiased and accurate information. EIA's annual energy and emissions reports, NREL's data on electricity, and NREL's data on vehicles are all good sources of information. Almost all of the numerical data in this book was derived from EIA and NREL.

Weinreb's Prior Work

Prior to writing this book, author Weinreb published 30 articles on climate change solutions for engineers. These readers are responsible for implementing decarbonization, and need accurate and unbiased information to do their work.

Where are the Engineers?

The engineers are at the carbon companies and the power companies, and they typically run circles around non-engineers when working with technical matters. This puts non-engineers at foundations, newspapers, and governments at a disadvantage. For example, when the IRA was passed, lawmakers and journalists failed to point out that it extended an existing policy that had previously produced only Mild Decarbonization. If the non-engineers had better tools, such as the previously described websites, for example, they would be more effective.

16. You Only Need to Look at One Graph to Solve the Climate Change Problem

The Intergovernmental Panel on Climate Change (IPCC) is an international group that studies climate change. Their 2022 Mitigation Report contains one illustration, shown below, that summarizes how to decarbonize.

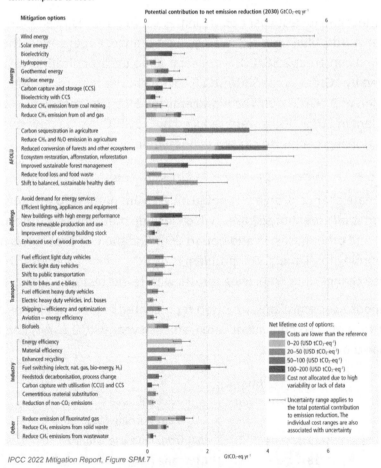

Figure 16.1: Decarbonization options and costs, according to IPCC.

This chart shows dozens of activities that reduce CO_2. For each activity, it uses a color-coded system to indicate the number of dollars needed to reduce CO_2 emissions by one metric ton ($/mtCO_2$).

Decarbonization opportunities that cost $1 to $20/mtCO_2$ are shown in light orange, opportunities that cost $20 to $50/mtCO_2$ are shown in orange, and opportunities with no decarbonization cost are shown in blue. No cost refers to moving to a lower-cost solution that also emits less CO_2.

The width of each horizontal bar indicates how much the world could reduce at each decarbonization cost in units of billions of metric tons of CO_2 equivalent each year ($GtCO_{2\text{-}eq}/yr$).

The easiest and lowest cost opportunities could potentially be tackled first. In other words, blue first, followed by light orange. For example, the world could first construct $2.5GtCO_2/yr$ of solar at no decarbonization cost (blue), followed by $1GtCO_2/yr$ at $20/mtCO_2$ cost (light orange), for a total reduction of $3.5GtCO_2/yr$. The world emitted 59 billion metric tons of CO_2 equivalent in 2019. If this were reduced by $3.5GtCO_2/yr$ via new solar farms, global greenhouse gas emissions would decrease by 6% (3.5 / 59).

CO_2 from Burning Fossil Fuels Is Only 64% of the Problem

The climate change problem is not just CO_2 from burning fossil fuels. The problem is *all* greenhouse gases, which include methane (e.g. rotting plants) and other gases, in addition to CO_2. And the CO_2 problem is not just from burning fossil fuels. The problem is *all* CO_2, which includes CO_2 from land use changes (e.g. replacing forests with fewer plants).

Greenhouse gas emissions are often represented in units of billions of metric tons of CO_2 "equivalent" emitted each year ($GtCO_{2\text{-}eq}/yr$) and are summarized below:

% of Total	$GtCO_2$-eq/yr	Greenhouse Gas
64%	38	CO_2 from burning fossil fuels
11%	7	CO_2 from land use change
18%	11	Methane (CH_4)
7%	4	Other

Figure 16.2: Global greenhouse gas emissions (Source: IPCC).

Global Greenhouse Gas Emissions Keeps Increasing

Greenhouse gas emissions are increasing globally, according to IPCC, as shown below.

Global emissions have continued to rise across all major groups of greenhouse gases.
IPCC 2022 Mitigation Report, Figure SPM.1

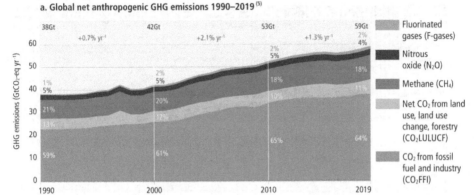

Figure 16.3: Greenhouse gas emissions are increasing (Source: IPCC).

CO_2 emissions are increasing partly due to 3% per year global GDP growth.

Figure 16.4: Carbon-based infrastructure resists being replaced for multiple reasons. These include employees who do not want to lose their jobs and lenders who want to be repaid.

CO_2 Emissions in the U.S. Are Not Decreasing

CO_2 emissions from the United States have remained somewhat constant over the last 6 years, as shown in the table below.

U.S. Greenhouse Gas Emissions and Sinks (MMT CO_2 Equivalents)

Gas/Source*	1990	2005	2016	2017	2018	2019	2020
CO$_2$	5,122.5	6,137.6	5,251.8	5,211.0	5,376.7	5,259.1	4,715.7
Fossil Fuel Combustion	4,731.2	5,752.0	4,909.6	4,853.3	4,989.3	4,852.3	4,342.7
Transportation	1,468.9	1,858.6	1,757.6	1,780.0	1,812.8	1,813.8	1,572.0
Electric Power Sector	1,820.0	2,400.1	1,808.9	1,732.0	1,752.9	1,606.1	1,439.0
Industrial	853.7	851.5	792.7	790.4	814.1	816.1	766.3
Residential	338.6	358.9	292.8	293.4	338.2	341.4	315.8
Commercial	228.3	227.1	231.5	232.0	245.8	250.7	226.8
U.S. Territories	21.7	55.9	26.0	25.5	25.5	24.3	22.7
Non-Energy Use of Fuels	112.2	128.9	99.5	112.6	128.9	126.8	121.0
Natural Gas Systems	31.9	24.9	29.8	31.1	32.4	38.7	35.4
Cement Production	33.5	46.2	39.4	40.3	39.0	40.9	40.7
Lime Production	11.7	14.6	12.6	12.9	13.1	12.1	11.3
Other Process Uses of Carbonates	6.2	7.5	10.8	9.9	7.4	9.8	9.8
Glass Production	2.3	2.4	2.1	2.0	2.0	1.9	1.9
Soda Ash Production	1.4	1.7	1.7	1.8	1.7	1.8	1.5
Carbon Dioxide Consumption	1.5	1.4	4.6	4.6	4.1	4.9	5.0
Incineration of Waste	12.9	13.3	14.4	13.2	13.3	12.9	13.1
Titanium Dioxide Production	1.2	1.8	1.7	1.7	1.5	1.5	1.3
Aluminum Production	6.8	4.1	1.3	1.2	1.5	1.9	1.7
Iron and Steel Production & Metallurgical Coke Production	104.7	70.1	43.6	40.6	42.6	43.1	37.7
Ferroalloy Production	2.2	1.4	1.8	2.0	2.1	1.6	1.4
Ammonia Production	13.0	9.2	10.2	11.1	12.2	12.3	12.7
Urea Consumption for Non-Agricultural Purposes	3.8	3.7	5.3	5.2	6.0	6.0	6.0
Phosphoric Acid Production	1.5	1.3	1.0	1.0	0.9	0.9	0.9
Petrochemical Production	21.6	27.4	28.1	28.9	29.3	30.7	30.0
Carbide Production and Consumption	0.2	0.2	0.2	0.2	0.2	0.2	0.2
Lead Production	0.5	0.6	0.5	0.5	0.5	0.5	0.5
Zinc Production	0.6	1.0	0.8	0.9	1.0	1.0	1.0
Petroleum Systems	9.6	12.0	21.9	25.0	37.3	46.7	30.2
Liming	4.7	4.3	3.1	3.1	2.2	2.4	2.4
Urea Fertilization	2.4	3.5	4.7	4.9	5.0	5.1	5.3
Coal Mining	4.6	4.2	2.8	3.1	3.1	3.0	2.2
International Bunker Fuels*	103.6	113.3	116.7	120.2	122.2	116.1	69.6
Wood Biomass, Ethanol, and Biodiesel Consumption*	219.4	230.7	316.9	312.7	319.8	317.2	291.6

Figure 16.5: Greenhouse gas emissions in the U.S. (Source: EIA).

Conclusion

In conclusion, 64% of global greenhouse gas emissions are caused by burning fossil fuels such as coal, natural gas, and gasoline. The rest are caused by things like land use changes (e.g. fewer trees) and more methane (e.g. thawing permafrost).

There are many affordable things one can do to reduce greenhouse gas emissions, as shown in one IPCC illustration.

17. How Do We Make Nuclear Fission Power Safer?

The primary ways of generating electricity without emitting CO_2 are solar farms, wind farms, hydroelectric dams, and nuclear fission power. Each of these involves challenges. For example, wind farms need windy land away from people, solar farms need cleared sunny land, and hydroelectric dams need sloped land with running water. Also, the output from wind farms and solar farms is often deficient due to little wind or sun. And one must contend with "not in my backyard" (NIMBY), which is when communities resist nearby construction.

Figure 17.1: Illustration of U.K. Hinkley Point C nuclear power station.

Can We Improve Fission Power?

Nuclear fission power *also* has challenges. More specifically it must contend with: (a) meltdown risk, (b) nuclear waste, (c) nuclear bomb proliferation risk, and (d) high cost. To address the first three concerns, a nation could establish stricter safety standards for both new and existing reactors. Otherwise, in many cases, new reactors are not likely to be built and existing reactors are likely to be shut down. Below is an example safety standard that might meet the satisfaction of the public:

- Loss of coolant does not result in a meltdown via negative temperature coefficient fuel.

- Nuclear fuel does not react with air or water and does not make them radioactive.

- The reactor does not produce waste that lasts longer than 300 years (e.g. thorium fuel).

- Fuel is proliferation resistant (e.g. thorium fuel).

- Existing reactors are *rebuilt* by the year 20xx to meet a new safety standard or shut down.

Safer Reactors Exist

The safest nuclear fission reactor in the world is probably HTR-PM in China. This uses an advanced nuclear fuel that does not melt when not cooled. An additive to the fuel provides what is called a "negative temperature coefficient." This means energy output decreases when its temperature exceeds normal operation.

There are two types of fission reactors. Those that do not melt when not cooled, and those that do. Currently, HTR-PM is the only commercially operating reactor with no-melt fuel. The disadvantage of HTR-PM is it costs approximately 20% more than traditional reactors.

Thorium fuel is similar to uranium fuel; however, it produces less nuclear waste and is less likely to be weaponized.

What Is an Acceptable National Fission Strategy?

If a nation wanted safer reactors quickly, they could buy HTR-PM reactors from China. Or, they could develop something similar and build locally. The steel reactor vessel costs relatively little; however, the containment building and the site construction are both costly in the U.S. and Europe. To reduce costs, one might streamline the certification and construction process after building several. Also, one could improve nuclear waste and proliferation risk with thorium fuel instead of uranium fuel. However, developing a thorium fuel capability might cost billions of dollars and take many years.

Conclusion

In conclusion, solar, wind, and hydroelectric power involve challenges. Therefore, we should consider spending billions of dollars on R&D to *improve* nuclear fission power to the extent required by the public.

18. How Do We Accelerate the Development of Nuclear Fusion Power?

In 1961, President Kennedy stated he wanted a man on the moon by the end of the decade. In response, a program was set up and funded. In theory, a government leader could do the same with nuclear fusion power. For example, they could state that commercial fusion must be operational by the end of the decade or within 5 to 10 years. This might seem unrealistic. However, notice how many "gadgets" the U.S. designed and manufactured between 1939 and 1945.

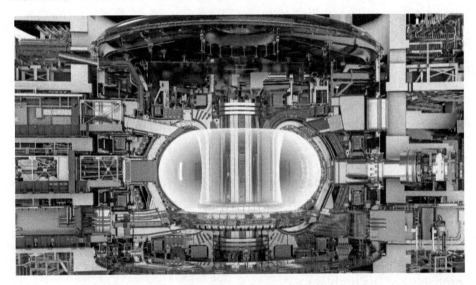

Figure 18.1: Nuclear fusion power station (illustration).

Fission and Fusion

There are two types of nuclear power: fission and fusion. Traditional nuclear power plants generate electricity with uranium via fission. However, this is not popular due to meltdown risk, nuclear waste, nuclear bomb proliferation risk, and cost. Fusion, on the other hand, does not have these issues; however, it is still in development. Typical fusion systems maintain a hot plasma in a donut-shaped reactor called a tokamak, as illustrated above.

Commercial Fusion

Commercial fusion refers to generating electricity at a cost comparable to electricity made with natural gas or coal. This requires the fusion reactor to run for long durations, without failure, and at a low cost.

Fusion Milestones

There are three fusion milestones that have yet to be met:

- Generate significant amounts of heat, expected ~2025.
- Generate electricity for less than a day, expected ~2035.
- Generate electricity commercially at low cost, expected ~2045.

Fusion Moonshot

Accelerating development within a large initiative is sometimes referred to as a "moonshot." A fusion moonshot could potentially accelerate commercial fusion. Subsequently, we should be asking top fusion scientists:

> *How much would it cost to achieve* <u>*commercial*</u> *fusion this decade? Where might this money go? Who could get this done?*

Heat is Probably Not the Problem

Reports in national media suggest current fusion reactors do not produce sufficient heat. This is true. However, heat increases when one increases the strength of the magnets, and stronger magnets were recently <u>developed at MIT</u>. These will be installed into a test reactor soon, and MIT hopes to demonstrate sufficient heat in 2025. In other words, heat is probably not the problem.

So what is the problem? Below are several.

Challenge #1: Reactor Build Time

Fusion test reactors typically take many years to build, and this is probably the greatest obstacle to commercial fusion. To move rapidly, one might need hundreds, or even thousands of engineers in places like China who can build and test quickly.

What does Elon Musk do after one of his rockets fails in spectacular fashion? He repeats. And after dozens of cycles, a working system emerges. To get commercial fusion working quickly, a similar approach might be needed.

Challenge #2: Component Longevity

To produce electricity at a low cost, a commercial fusion reactor would need to run for long durations without failure. To ensure longevity, engineers could run individual components in test fixtures at maximum power, or more, to see how and when they break, and then improve as needed. This might sound easy; however, doing this with many components takes time and requires many engineers. And if a delicate component, such as a magnet, fails prematurely on a regular basis, a remedy might not be quick or easy.

Challenge #3: Disposable Plasma Confinement Chamber

The heat from a fusion reactor core needs to be moved outward, to create steam, to press on turbine fan blades, to produce electricity. The easiest way to do this is to pump fluids, such as molten lead or molten salt, toward the hot plasma, and then outward.

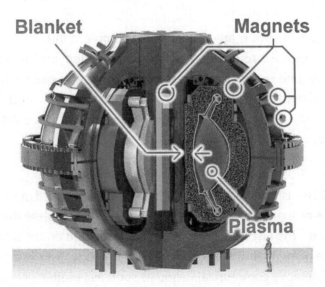

Figure 18.2: Plasma is surrounded by a reactor "blanket" which removes heat and absorbs neutron radiation.

Neutron radiation from hot plasma weakens surrounding metal for about one meter of penetration depth. Subsequently, the plasma confinement chamber would need to be replaced approximately once a year. This chamber is labeled "blanket" in the above illustration. In other words, one might need to fabricate 50 of these chambers over a 50-year period. And fabricating these at low cost would probably require automation and molded processes. For example, an industrial robot might weld together molded metal panels affixed to a jig.

It is not difficult for a team of engineers, or even one engineer, to design the mechanics of how a fusion reactor fits together. Also, multiple teams could create multiple designs that are later selected or merged after being reviewed. However, it is not clear how to identify the best design. And after committing to one design, it might take many years to build and test.

To help verify designs, one could build prototypes *quickly* that are 1 to $10m^3$ in size. These might not include magnets, and might not maintain the plasma. However, they could verify assembly of molded panels via industrial robots, verify pumping of fluids at high pressure, verify moving heat, and verify replacing internal components via industrial robots.

To Plan or Not To Plan?

There are two ways to manage a large development initiative. The traditional method is to develop a plan, get it funded, and implement. Alternatively, one can set goals, assemble a top team, give them authority, provide funding, and get out of their way. The traditional method works well if one knows what needs to be done. Unfortunately, commercial fusion is not well understood.

Achieve Commercial Fusion as Soon as Possible

ITER is a $25B fusion reactor development program based in France. Their reactor was designed 20 years ago and is currently obsolete due to advances over the last two decades. If ITER had been driven by a goal instead of a plan, it would probably be further along. An example goal might be, "Achieve commercial fusion as soon as possible given $1B/yr."

How Might a Foundation Accelerate Fusion?

If a philanthropic foundation wanted to accelerate the development of fusion power with $100M, for example, how might it proceed? Below is one possible approach.

- Establish a blue ribbon panel with 5 to 15 of the world's top fusion scientists and engineers.

- Establish a goal, such as "achieve commercial fusion this decade."

- Set up a management team, possibly within a foundation or institution, that manages the initiative. More specifically, they oversee contracts, purchase orders, invoices, and money.

- The blue ribbon panel determines how to spend money, and the management team is instructed to provide them with maximum support. In other words, power is placed in the hands of the panel and not the management team. And cash is put into the hands of the management team, not the panel.

- All scientists and engineers who receive money are required to make produced materials open source (e.g. spreadsheets, designs, simulations, and test data). Subsequently, anyone can view, copy, modify and use it in any way; at no cost. Materials are placed on the internet, and anyone is welcome to review, rework, or improve. Transparency improves productivity since problems are identified more quickly.

- Scientists and engineers at the world's top 10 fusion research organizations are invited to participate. Many are motivated since they receive money in return for work, and they can use produced materials.

- The initiative produces multiple paper-only reactor designs, simulations, simple prototypes of components, and proposals for more work. However, the initiative does not produce an actual physical reactor. For that, one would need more money.

How Is This Different?

After the typical fusion R&D initiative commits to one design and begins construction, money and talent focus on building the test reactor instead of more design. Also, most fusion research programs focus on the first two milestones (i.e. more heat, remove heat) as opposed to commercial fusion (i.e. low cost, reliable, serviceable, automated assembly). Therefore, an initiative that focuses on design-only, open source, cost reduction, component longevity, and automated fabrication/maintenance would be different from existing fusion development initiatives.

When to Profit?

If the above initiative ultimately led to a commercial fusion reactor, its design could potentially be licensed for manufacture. Licensing revenue could then be fed back to the organizations that designed it. The world's fusion organizations know this. Therefore, they might be inclined to convert an open-source initiative to proprietary. For example, top people might stop contributing to open source when it is 90% complete, and do the last 10% as proprietary. In other words, a philanthropic foundation might get this started open source. However, ultimately, the financial interests of governments, investors, companies, and fusion research institutions might cause them to lose interest in open source when close to complete (which would be okay).

Getting it Done

Why would this initiative not be funded originally by commercial investors? That is already happening; however, those efforts are not expected to produce commercial fusion before 2040.

Why would this initiative not be funded originally by government? That is already happening too. However, national interests and emphasis on plan are not expected to produce commercial fusion any time soon.

To accelerate fusion development, one might initially need a sponsor who is *not* looking for a return on investment, requires transparency, is willing to give power to top people, and encourages participation across national boundaries.

In conclusion, wealthy people concerned about climate change should consider accelerating the development of fusion power.

19. Climate Change and China

If climate change were a puzzle, then China would probably be the largest piece in the center of the board. This is due to multiple reasons: (a) China emits more CO_2 than any other nation, in part due to making things for others, (b) China's mass production of solar and wind power equipment has reduced green electricity costs significantly, (c) China developed HTR-PM, the safest nuclear reactor in the world, (d) China has built more nuclear reactors in the last five years than any other nation, (e) China's nuclear reactors are likely to become the lowest cost way to decarbonize high-temperature manufacturing, (f) China is likely to become the largest supplier of equipment that makes green energy, and (g) China is likely to drive down the cost of decarbonization more than any other nation via factory mass production.

China Is Decarbonizing at the Pace of a Snail

China's CO_2 emissions keep going up, as shown underline below. This is in part due to their gross domestic product, which increases by approximately underline 6% each year.

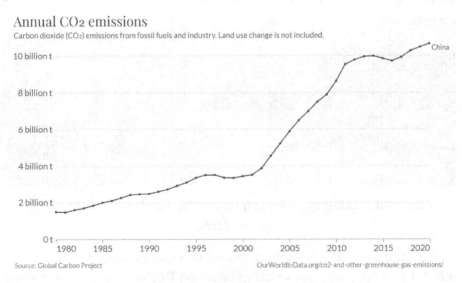

Annual CO2 emissions

Carbon dioxide (CO₂) emissions from fossil fuels and industry. Land use change is not included.

Source: Global Carbon Project

OurWorldInData.org/co2-and-other-greenhouse-gas-emissions/

Figure 19.1: Annual CO₂ emissions from China.

In China, the amount of green electricity as a percentage of total increased from 29% to 32% over the last 6 years. In other words, China's electricity is decarbonizing at a rate of 0.7% each year ((32.6% - 28.9%) / 5yrs).

Alternatively, if China fully decarbonized its electricity over 10 years, for example, this increase would be 7% each year ((100% - 32%) / 10yrs)).

China is decarbonizing electricity at the pace of a snail. And the U.S. is not doing better.

What Might Cause China to Decarbonize More Quickly?

As noted previously, warmer air leads to dryer land, dryer land leads to less food, and less food leads to higher food prices. Spending money today on greener electricity, in theory, could save money tomorrow in multiple ways, including lower food costs. There is a saying, "The key to a man's heart is his stomach." Perhaps this applies to climate change?

China experienced severe droughts in 2022, leading to low water levels in rivers and lakes. It is possible food shortages in China will worsen, partly due to climate change, and lead to more decarbonization. However, it is unclear when and to what extent this might occur.

Figure 19.2: Dried-up canal in a rural village on Lantau Island, Hong Kong, China.

California in the U.S. spends more money on decarbonization than any other U.S. state, partly due to daily images on TV showing low water levels in California reservoirs. Perhaps similar images on China's TV will have a similar effect.

20. Green Electricity in the United States

The U.S. generates <u>22%</u> of its electricity from coal, and 38% from natural gas. If these were replaced with green electricity (e.g. solar, wind, hydro), CO_2 emissions from all sources (e.g. cars, factories, electricity) in the U.S. would decrease approximately by 30% (<u>1.5Gt / 5Gt</u>).

Currently, 38% of U.S. electricity is already "green." This includes 19% from nuclear, 9% from wind, 6% from hydroelectric dams, and 4% from solar. However, if one looks at <u>select states</u>, they will see a different picture, as shown in the <u>table</u> below.

Region	Total GREEN	Nuclear	Hydro	Small + Utility Solar	Wind	Utility Solar	Small Solar
USA Total	38.4%	18.9%	6.3%	4.0%	9.2%	2.8%	1.2%
California (D)	50.2%	8.3%	7.4%	26.6%	7.9%	17.4%	9.2%
Texas (R)	32.6%	8.3%	0.2%	3.4%	20.7%	2.9%	0.5%
North Carolina (R)	46.9%	32.9%	5.8%	7.9%	0.4%	7.5%	0.4%
Florida (D)	16.0%	11.5%	0.1%	4.5%	0.0%	3.7%	0.8%
Nevada (D)	23.4%	0.0%	4.5%	18.0%	0.8%	15.8%	2.3%
Arizona (R)	44.8%	29.3%	5.4%	8.7%	1.5%	6.1%	2.6%
Massachusetts (D)	28.6%	0.0%	4.2%	23.3%	1.0%	9.2%	14.2%
New York (D)	54.3%	24.9%	22.3%	3.6%	3.4%	1.0%	2.7%
New Mexico (D)	36.8%	0.0%	0.5%	6.0%	30.3%	4.9%	1.1%

Figure 20.1: Electricity generation as a percentage of total electricity (Source: U.S. EIA 2021).

"Utility solar" typically refers to solar farms with greater than 1-megawatt capacity ($\geq$ 1MW), and "small solar" typically refers to solar panels on buildings.

California is evenly balanced among solar, wind, hydro, and nuclear. They are also considering replacing their nuclear power with solar and wind power, which is feasible to an extent. On the other hand, Massachusetts shut down its nuclear power plants without replacement and is, therefore, less green than average. In general, states strong in nuclear are also more green.

Texas and New Mexico rely heavily on wind power due to an ample wind supply far from buildings. New York relies heavily on hydroelectric power due to hydroelectric dams in Canada and Niagara Falls. Nevada and California rely heavily on solar farms due to an ample supply of cleared, sunny unused land.

Approximately 70% of utility-scale solar power in the U.S. is generated by six states. Three of them lean to the political left (e.g. CA, FL, NV) and three lean to the political right (i.e. TX, NC, AZ). In other words, solar is popular with both the political left and right.

Figure 20.2: Solar farm and wind farm.

When homeowners generate their own electricity via solar panels, they are often compensated at the retail electricity generation plus distribution price. Subsequently, there is more incentive to install residential solar in states with high electricity prices. For example, Massachusetts and California residential electricity is approximately 60% higher than the national average (e.g. 23¢/kWh vs. 14¢/kWh, May 2021). This has driven Massachusetts residential solar to 14% of state electricity and driven California residential solar to 9% of state electricity. Both of these are high relative to the national average of 1.2%.

Local lawmakers can increase carbon-based electricity prices via a variety of techniques, such as creating a regional natural gas shortage by not building pipes that carry natural gas. Some might consider this a good way to decarbonize. However, it is costly relative to other techniques. The lowest cost way to decarbonize is to require power companies to buy increasing amounts of green electricity.

U.S. Electricity Expansion During 2022

The below map shows *new* utility scale (≥ 1MW) power generation facilities that are expected to be completed in the U.S. between May 2022 and April 2023. The area of each circle is proportional to power output. Yellow refers to solar farms, green refers to wind farms, and tan refers to natural gas-based power plants.

Figure 6.1.C. Utility-Scale Generating Units Planned to Come Online from May 2022 to April 2023

Sources: U.S. Energy Information Administration, Form EIA-860, 'Annual Electric Generator Report' and Form EIA-860M, 'Monthly Update to the Annual Electric Generator Report.'

Figure 20.3: New utility scale (≥ 1MW) power generation facilities expected to be completed between May 2022 and April 2023.

Green Electricity Saturation

Green electricity saturation occurs when one discards electricity due to having enough. In other words, if electricity from solar, wind, hydro, *and* nuclear exceeds what is needed, the most costly source is typically asked to reduce output.

California is currently bumping into saturation, partly due to significant solar and wind capacity. In other words, California sometimes discards electricity from solar and wind farms when both sunny and windy, and when total electricity consumption is low.

Discarding some electricity is okay since it is often less costly to over-build solar or wind power with occasional discarding than to add battery storage.

One might reach saturation with a relatively small amount of additional solar if already significantly covered by wind/hydro/nuclear. Alternatively, one might be able to construct many solar farms before reaching saturation if only lightly covered by wind/hydro/nuclear.

Consumption Varies Throughout the Day, Week, and Year

The graphs below show how the consumption of electricity in the U.S. varies throughout the day, week and year. Consumption is lower at night and when outdoor temperatures require little heating or air conditioning (e.g. 75°F/24°C). Over a year, U.S. electricity consumption ranges between 320GW and 680GW; and averages 470GW.

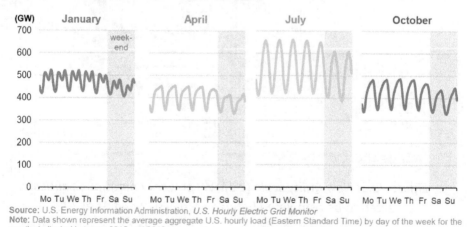

Figure 20.4: U.S. electricity consumption during selected months.

Bumping Into Saturation

U.S green electricity *production* capacity is 410GW when solar power and wind power are at maximum levels. This includes 95GW from nuclear, 80GW from hydro, 98GW from solar, and 137GW from wind.

Alternatively, *consumption* at midday, during the spring and fall, is 450GW. In other words, the U.S. is close to saturation in the spring and fall, when solar and wind power are at maximum. However, the U.S. rarely meets all of these conditions at the same time.

	Electricity Consumption (GW)				Maximum Electricity Production (GW)				
Region	Summer Min Load	Summer Max Load	Spring Min Load	Spring Max Load	Total GREEN	Nuclear	Hydro	Small + Utility Solar	Wind
USA Total	420	650	350	450	410	95	80	98	137
California (D)	28	48	25	33	38	2	10	19	6
Texas (R)	37	63	29	40	52	5	1	11	36

Figure 20.5: Minimum and maximum U.S. consumption in spring and summer, and maximum green electricity production, in gigawatt units (Source: EIA Feb 2020).

If one looks at different regions, they are likely to see a different picture. For example, California and Texas are already bumping into saturation. California *consumption* at midday during the spring is 33GW, and maximum green electricity *production* is 38GW. Alternatively, Texas consumption at midday during the spring is 40GW, and maximum green electricity production is 52GW. This might seem encouraging. However, it is rare for wind to be at maximum, while sunny, while HVAC is off.

Figure 20.6: Windfarms in Texas occasionally discard electricity.

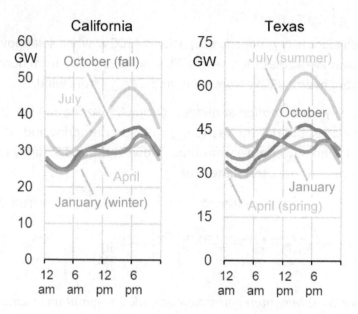

Figure 20.7: Total electricity consumption over a 24-hour period in California and Texas (Source: EIA Feb 2020).

Some Saturation Is OK

Saturation might seem wasteful; however, it is not as bad as it sounds. Let's look at an example case to gain a better understanding. We begin by assuming electricity from solar is 40% of the total, and 30% of solar power is discarded 25% of the time. The average U.S. home consumes 10,000 kWh a year, and if solar wholesale electricity generation costs 3¢/kWh, then discarding in this manner would cost $9 per-house-per-year ($0.03 x 10,000 x 40% x 30% x 25%).

Figure 20.8: Carbon-based electricity is not generated when renewables are in saturation.

A Day in the Year 2050

The graphs below show expected sources of electricity over a 24-hour cycle in the year 2050, in three U.S. regions. Solar power is shown in yellow, wind power is shown in green, hydroelectric power is shown in dark blue, nuclear power is shown in dark red, natural gas-based electricity is shown in light blue, and coal-based electricity is shown in gray.

The West is expected to rely heavily on solar, wind, and hydro; with little storage. California is expected to rely mostly on solar and battery storage. And the Southeast is expected to rely mostly on solar, nuclear, and natural gas.

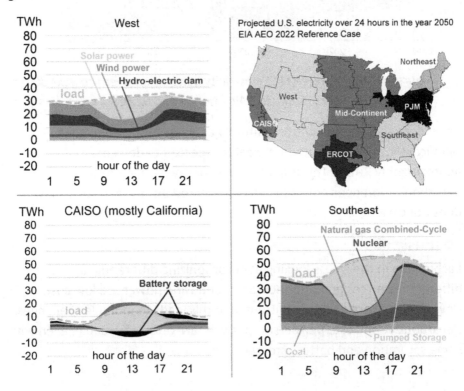

Figure 20.9: Projected sources of electricity over a 24 hour cycle in the year 2050 (Source: EIA Outlook 2022).

U.S. 30-Year Projection

The following graph is the official U.S. government projection for U.S. electricity over the next 30 years, based on economic and market behavior.

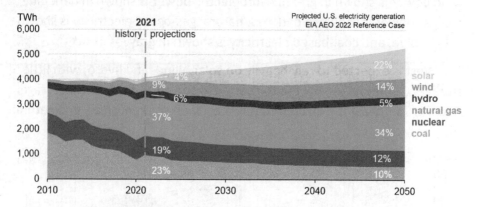

Figure 20.10: Projected U.S. electricity generation over the next 30 years (Source: EIA Outlook Feb 2022).

As one can see, electricity from natural gas is not expected to change significantly, and electricity from coal is expected to decrease approximately 2-fold. This is another way of saying significant decarbonization does not occur unless required by law, and such a law does not exist.

Conclusion

Each region in the U.S. is looking at decarbonizing differently due to different resources and priorities. Solar and wind power are low cost. However, they are also intermittent, and this leads to multiple challenges. Decarbonization costs-per-person-per-year are often affordable, even with some saturation and battery storage.

21. The Economics of Climate Change

Our civilization is looking at replacing carbon-based infrastructure with infrastructure that does not emit CO_2. This includes:

- Facilities that generate electrical power (e.g. solar, wind, hydro).
- Factories that make chemicals (e.g. hydrogen, ammonia).
- Factories that make materials (e.g. plastics, metals, ceramics, cement).
- Vehicles (e.g. electric vehicles).

Infrastructure Is Paid for with Borrowed Money

Most infrastructure is paid for with money borrowed from banks and bonds. Later, these are repaid with revenue generated by the infrastructure. For example, a bank loan might initially fund solar farm construction, while farm electricity sales repays the loan over 30 years.

Economically, decarbonization is like a nation buying one new house each year, where the house represents all green infrastructure built that year. The nation ends up with one "house" after year #1, two after year #2, etc.

Also, each house has a mortgage. Subsequently, the nation pays one mortgage after year #1, two after year #2, etc. The mortgage payments show up as an increase in the costs of goods and services. And one can calculate this increase in units of dollars-per-person-per-year.

Keep Decarbonization Tolerable

Evidence of climate change increases each year; therefore, *tolerance* of decarbonization costs are also likely to increase. To decarbonize, costs need to stay below the tolerance of costs as one goes through time. For this reason, a nation might decarbonize in the lowest cost order. For example, tackle $10/mtCO_2$ projects first, followed by $13/mtCO_2$, etc. As we noted previously, $/mtCO_2$ refers to the number of dollars spent to reduce CO_2 emissions by one ton. If we apply this to the house analogy, the first house is cheap, and each additional house is more costly.

The Green Premium

Electricity made without emitting CO_2 is typically referred to as "green electricity." Example sources are solar farms, wind farms, hydroelectric dams, and nuclear power plants. Alternatively, carbon-based electricity is typically made by burning natural gas or coal.

The difference in the cost of the green option, which does not emit CO_2 and the carbon-based option is referred to as the "green premium." For example, if electricity from a solar farm costs 4¢/kWh and the natural gas fuel it replaces costs 3¢/kWh, the green premium would be approximately 1¢/kWh.

In some cases, 0.1 to 1¢/kWh is added to the cost of the carbon-based fuel to cover additional expenses (i.e. variable costs).

The green premium for solar and wind farms is typically between -1¢/kWh and +3¢/kWh. Negative values refer to green electricity that costs less than the natural gas or coal fuel it replaces. This is rare; however, it does occasionally occur due to fuel shortages that increase fuel prices.

Government Subsidies are Tricky

Consumers typically disfavor green products because they cost more. However, in theory, government can change this by paying a portion. The goal is to cross over a tipping point where the subsidized green product costs less than the carbon-based product. This works fine in theory; however, prices of both green and carbon-based products typically vary over time and place. For example, the price of natural gas in the U.S. varied between 2¢ and 4¢/kWh between 2017 and 2021 (i.e. fuel cost per kWh of electricity) and was 20% more in California than nearby Utah.

Due to these fluctuations, fixed subsidies are often not helpful or are too helpful. For example, if the green premium starts at +1.5¢, then lowering it to +0.5¢ with a 1¢ subsidy still does not make the green product cheaper. Or if the green premium starts at +0.5¢, then lowering it to -0.5¢ with a 1¢ subsidy wastes public money.

Subsidizing electricity is tricky since fuel consumption decreases when it is replaced by renewables. And this causes fuel prices to decrease and green premiums to increase, which leads to an ineffective subsidy. In other words, if the subsidy is working, it will eventually stop working.

Instead of subsidies, one can *require* power companies to obtain more green electricity each year. This avoids the above-stated problems, and power company engineers can implement at the lowest cost.

Already, many U.S. states have green electricity requirements. They are commonly referred to as "Renewable Portfolio Standards" (RPS). However, they are not federal and are often mild relative to what is needed.

Decarbonization Is Often Driven by Price, Not by Government

In many cases, CO_2 is reduced to save money, and not to reduce CO_2. For example, between 2005 and 2019, U.S. CO_2 emissions decreased by 0.86 billion tons ($0.86GtCO_2/yr$). One might think this was intentional. However, 70% of this was due to replacing coal with lower-cost natural gas. In another example, wind and solar farm construction surged in 2022, driven by high natural gas and coal prices.

Historically, markets have affected CO_2 more than government.

Figure 21.1: Coal powered the industrial revolution and helped to build our modern society. Many people do not like coal; however, if it did not exist, we and our cities would probably not be here.

The Entanglement of Fuel Price and Decarbonization

The graph below shows the price of natural gas in the U.S. over the last 25 years.

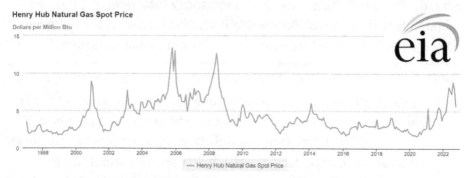

Figure 21.2: U.S. natural gas price in units of $/MMBtu (Source: EIA)

The supply of natural gas in the U.S. was strong between 2010 and 2021, partly due to fracking. However, shortages in 2022 caused its price to increase. And this caused green premiums to *decrease*, which led to more decarbonization. However, in future years, fuel prices are likely to decrease due to more green electricity that reduces fuel consumption, which reduces fuel price.

In other words, fuel shortages in 2022 led to more decarbonization; however, new laws will be needed to decarbonize further.

*Figure 21.3: Demand for carbon-based fuels was high in 2022, and this encouraged nations to build **more** carbon-based infrastructure.*

22. The Economics of Green Electricity

Reports often compare the cost of electricity from a new solar farm or a new wind farm with the cost of electricity from a *new* natural gas or coal-fired power plant. However, this is not what happens. Instead, the carbon plant has already been built and paid for, and it burns less fuel when its electricity is *replaced* with intermittent green electricity. Also, the carbon plant is needed when the sun goes down or the wind stops blowing.

The U.S. Southwest is Sunny and the Middle is Windy

The cost of fuel varies over time and place. Also, the cost of electricity from wind and solar power varies depending on the region since some are sunnier and others are windier. For example, the U.S. South West is often sunny, and the middle part of the U.S. is often windy. For details, one can refer to a <u>Solar Map</u> or a <u>Wind Map</u>, examples of which are shown below.

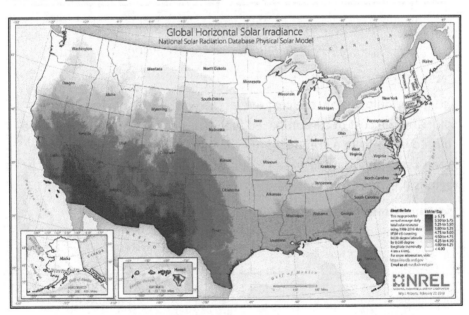

Figure 22.1: Average sunshine in units of heat energy-per-square-meter-per-day for a surface that constantly faces the sun.

Figure 22.2: Average wind velocity at 80m above the surface in units of meters-per-second.

Green Premium Math

The tables below show the cost of electricity from solar farms in green-color and the cost of carbon-based fuel in red-color. One subtracts a red-colored value from a green-colored value to calculate the approximate green premium. As one can see, the cost of electricity is less in sunny regions (i.e. more kWh/m^2/day).

Solar Farm Electricity Cost[1]

Resource Class	Heat Energy (kWh/m^2/ Day)	Mean AC Capacity Factor	U.S. Area (sq. km)	2022 NREL LCOE Cost $0.01/kWh
1	> 5.75	33%	216,551	3.3¢
2	5.5–5.75	32%	349,894	3.4¢
3	5.25–5.5	30%	372,764	3.5¢
4	5–5.25	29%	497,444	3.7¢
5	4.75–5	27%	779,720	3.9¢
6	4.5–4.75	26%	870,218	4.1¢
7	4.25–4.5	25%	727,918	4.2¢
8	4–4.25	23%	828,438	4.4¢
9	3.75–4	22%	794,496	4.6¢
10	< 3.75	20%	163,120	5.0¢

Cost of Natural Gas fuel used to Generate Electricity[2]

($0.01/kWh)	2017	2018	2019	2020	2021
USA avg	2.6¢	2.8¢	2.2¢	1.9¢	3.9¢
Calif.	2.8¢	3.5¢	2.9¢	2.5¢	4.2¢
Utah	2.6¢	2.4¢	2.4¢	2.0¢	3.5¢

Cost of Coal fuel used to Generate Electricity[3]

($0.01/kWh)	2017	2018	2019	2020
USA avg	2.2¢	2.2¢	2.2¢	2.0¢

1) US, wholesale, no tax credits, includes $0.005/kWh for power wires., US NREL 2022, https://atb.nrel.gov/electricity/2022/index
2) US, wholesale, power plant already built, 44% eff. elect. gen., https://www.eia.gov/dnav/ng/ng_sum_lsum_dcu_SCA_a.htm
3) US, wholesale, coal delivered to power sector, EIA 2022, https://www.eia.gov/energyexplained/coal/prices-and-outlook.php

Figure 22.3: Cost of electricity from solar farms and carbon sources.

Also, one can do this with wind power via the tables below.

Wind Farm Electricity Cost[1]

Resource Class	Wind Speed Range (m/s)	2022 NREL LCOE Cost $0.01/kWh
1	> 9.0	3.2¢
2	8.8 - 9.0	3.4¢
3	8.6 - 8.8	3.5¢
4	8.4 - 8.6	3.5¢
5	8.1 - 8.4	3.6¢
6	7.6 - 8.1	3.8¢
7	7.1 - 7.6	4.1¢
8	6.5 - 7.1	4.6¢
9	5.9 - 6.5	5.4¢
10	0 - 5.9	8.1¢

Cost of Natural Gas fuel used to Generate Electricity[2]

($0.01/kWh)	2017	2018	2019	2020	2021
USA avg	2.6¢	2.8¢	2.2¢	1.9¢	3.9¢
Calif.	2.8¢	3.5¢	2.9¢	2.5¢	4.2¢
Utah	2.6¢	2.4¢	2.4¢	2.0¢	3.5¢

Cost of Coal fuel used to Generate Electricity[3]

($0.01/kWh)	2017	2018	2019	2020
USA avg	2.2¢	2.2¢	2.2¢	2.0¢

1) US, wholesale, no tax credits, includes $0.005/kWh for power wires., NREL 2022, https://atb.nrel.gov/electricity/2022/index
2) US, wholesale, power plant already built, 44% eff. elect. gen., https://www.eia.gov/dnav/ng/ng_sum_lsum_dcu_SCA_a.htm
3) US, wholesale, coal delivered to power sector, EIA 2022, https://www.eia.gov/energyexplained/coal/prices-and-outlook.php

Figure 22.4: Cost of electricity from wind farms and carbon sources.

The above green-colored values reflect the *wholesale* cost to generate electricity. When calculating green premiums, one can ignore *residential retail* prices since a difference can be calculated by subtracting two wholesale values. For reference, U.S. *residential retail* is typically 7¢/kWh for generation and 7¢/kWh for distribution (May 2021 EIA).

Figure 22.5: Wind farms typically generate electricity at a low cost.

Many nations use subsidies to lower the green premium. For example, the U.S. government subsidizes green electricity by approximately 1¢/kWh as of Sept 2022. This is helpful; however, subsidized green electricity still costs more than carbon-based sources when natural gas and coal fuel prices are low. The green-colored values in the above tables do not include subsidies.

If Texas is windy and Oklahoma is not, more power wires from Texas windmills to Oklahoma cities would be helpful. The cost of adding more wires typically ranges between 0.1¢ and 1¢/kWh. The green-colored values in the above tables include 0.5¢/kWh for more power wires.

In summary, green premiums in the U.S. typically vary between -1¢/kWh and +3¢/kWh when replacing coal or natural gas-based electricity with solar or wind power.

Electricity Economics

The revenue at a carbon-based power plant is the sum of the following components: (a) fuel cost, (b) mortgage on the original construction, (c) fixed expenses that do not change when output power changes, (d) variable expenses proportional to output power, and (e) profit to the owner. When a carbon-based facility reduces output power due to being replaced by green electricity, savings are mostly from lower fuel costs.

Consumers typically see an increase in the cost of goods and services when electricity prices increase. This is due to competition that pushes the price of goods and services down to approximately 8% more than costs. In other words, a company's profit is 8% of revenue, on average.

If the cost of wholesale electricity increased, one's residential electric bill would increase, as well as the cost of goods and services that consume electricity. Residential electricity is approximately 20% of all electricity.

Figure 22.6: Power plants burn natural gas to produce electricity.

Decarbonization Math ($/mtCO₂)

When replacing *coal-based* electricity with green electricity, the decarbonization cost is approximately $10 per metric ton of CO_2 avoided per 1¢/kWh of green premium.

When replacing *natural gas-based* electricity with green electricity, the decarbonization cost is approximately $24 per metric ton of CO_2 avoided per 1¢/kWh of green premium.

For example, if green electricity costs 1.5¢/kWh more than the natural gas fuel it replaces, the decarbonization cost is approximately $36/mtCO₂ ($24 x 1.5¢ / 1¢). Or if green electricity costs 2.5¢/kWh more than the *coal* fuel it replaces, the decarbonization cost is approximately $25/mtCO₂ ($10 x 2.5¢ / 1¢).

Coal often costs less than natural gas; however, coal's CO_2 emissions are greater. Therefore, the cost to avoid a ton of CO_2 is often less when replacing coal, as shown in the below table.

Fuel Replaced	Decarbonization Cost ($/mtCO₂)	Green Premium ($/kWh)	Green Premium (¢/kWh)
Coal	$5	$0.005	0.5¢
	$10	$0.010	1¢
	$20	$0.020	2¢
	$30	$0.030	3¢
	$40	$0.040	4¢
Natural Gas	$12	$0.005	0.5¢
	$24	$0.010	1¢
	$48	$0.020	2¢
	$73	$0.030	3¢

Figure 22.7: Decarbonization cost ($/mtCO₂) is proportional to green premium ($/kWh).

Carbon Capture and Sequestration (CCS) Is Expensive

An exhaust gas stream is produced when one burns natural gas or coal. Typically 3% to 15% of this is CO_2, and the rest is mostly nitrogen (N_2). It is possible to extract the CO_2 from this stream, pump it to a different location, and store it underground. This is referred to as "carbon capture and sequestration" (CCS).

Storing CO_2 might seem nifty; however, it is expensive and, therefore, not competitive with other methods of decarbonization. Also, it requires a pipe network that connects many sources of CO_2 to one or more storage sites, and this network does not exist.

CCS is likely to unfold to some extent, but only after lower cost decarbonization opportunities have been exhausted, perhaps 5 to 15 years from now. For details, see the "Carbon, Capture and Sequestration" chapter.

Decarbonization Does Not Occur Unless Required by Law

Consumers buy the lowest cost solution, independent of CO_2 emissions. This is consistent with economic theory and observed behavior. In other words, significant decarbonization does not occur unless the green option costs less, or decarbonization is required by law. And the green option rarely costs less.

What Does This Cost?

If electricity decarbonization was required by law, what would it cost? The average American home consumes 10,000kWh of electricity each year, and if this increased 2¢/kWh due to decarbonization, for example, it would increase by $200 for one year ($0.02 x 10,000). However, $200 corresponds to 100% of electricity, and we are looking at decarbonizing a small fraction each year. For example, if 6% were decarbonized each year over 9 years, then the average *annual* (not monthly) residential electric bill would be $12 higher than today in year #1 (6% x $200) and $108 higher than today in year #9 (6% x $200 x 9yrs). If the house supported 4 people, then additional cost-per-person-per-year in year #1 would be $3 ($12 / 4 people). In summary, green electricity is often affordable.

Replace Carbon, Do Not Block Carbon

Environmentalists sometimes advocate restricting the production of carbon-based fuels. For example, they might advocate reducing the number of drilling permits for natural gas. At first glance, this might seem like a reasonable way to decarbonize. However, it does not decarbonize at the lowest cost. Instead, it leads to fuel shortages, high fuel prices, inflation, high-interest rates, and recession risk.

To decarbonize at the lowest cost, one must build a solar farm *before* reducing the output of the carbon-based power plant. In other words, *replace* carbon, do not block carbon.

Figure 22.8: Existing coal-based electrical power plants can easily reduce output when green electricity is available.

Block vs. Replace

Now, let's compare block with replace. Suppose we block carbon and create an oil shortage that causes the price to increase by $10 per barrel. The U.S. consumes 7.2B barrels each year; therefore, this would cost $72B per year.

Alternatively, one could use the $72B to build solar farms. They cost approximately $1.12-per-watt (CAPEX, NREL, 2022). Therefore, one could build 64GW of solar with $72B ($1.12 x 64GW). Over a year, they typically produce 2,334 watt-hours of electricity for each watt of capacity. Therefore, this would produce 149 TWh of electricity each year (64GW x 2,334).

When one replaces 1 TWh of natural gas-based electricity with green electricity, 0.41 million tons of CO_2 are not emitted. Therefore, this would reduce CO_2 by 61 million tons each year (149 TWh x 0.41 $MtCO_2$). One can typically sell electricity wholesale for approximately $0.03/kWh. Therefore, this would produce 4.5 billion dollars of revenue each year ($0.03 x 149e12). What would you prefer?

a) Pay $72B with little benefit.
b) Pay $72B to reduce CO_2 by 61Mt/yr and receive $4.5B/yr for 30 years.

Can Society as a Whole Do Math?

The above solar farm example involves four constants (i.e. $1.12, 2234, $0.03, 0.41), several multiplications, and several divisions. Wind farm math is similar, yet with different constants. And that's it. This is all the math one needs to know to understand lowest-cost decarbonization. If journalists taught this to the public, resolving climate change would be more likely.

Figure 22.9: The younger generation is concerned about the planet they aim to inherent.

Economic Ignorance Puts the World in Danger

Government policy sometimes does not make sense in part due to: (a) senior economists not being present when important policies are formulated, (b) high-level people in government not understanding economics, (c) journalists not being familiar with economics, and (d) economics not being explained well in national media.

Ultimately, economic ignorance puts the world in danger.

23. The Economics of Green Heat

Decarbonizing most electricity could be done by building more solar, wind and hydro at reasonable costs. However, this still leaves manufacturing to be decarbonized.

Many manufacturing processes use high-temperature heat to make chemicals (e.g. hydrogen, ammonia) and to make materials (e.g. plastics, metals, ceramics, glass, cement).

When creating high temperatures without emitting CO_2, the lowest-cost option is to use heat directly from a nuclear fission reactor. Unfortunately, the alternatives tend to be costly (e.g. solar, wind, and hydro). Co-locating fission and manufacturing is currently not being done. However, if one is looking for lowest-cost high-temperature green manufacturing, this is probably it.

Nations averse to nuclear will probably import before building reactors at home. In other words, they will probably use solar, wind, and hydro to decarbonize most of their electricity; and use someone else's nuclear power to obtain green materials at the lowest cost.

Figure 23.1: Heat is often moved by pumping steam within pipes

China Is Comfortable with Nuclear Power and Making Money

The amount of electricity produced by nuclear fission power in China doubles every 5 years, as shown below. China builds more nuclear reactors each year than any other nation and will probably be the first to export cheap green materials made directly with nuclear reactor heat. They are motivated to do this since it enables them to gain wealth via export.

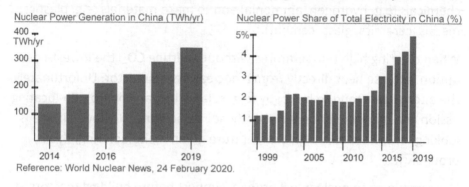

Figure 23.2: Nuclear power in China (Source: Wikipedia)

Does the U.S. or Europe Want to Compete in Green Heat?

Nuclear reactors in the U.S. and Europe cost three times more than that in China ($6K vs $2K/kW$_e$). If the U.S or Europe wanted to be more competitive, they could: (a) reduce the cost of fission via standardization, commoditization, and automated site construction, (b) improve fission with more R&D, and (c) accelerate fusion development with more money.

Heat Weights and Measures

Heat is often represented in units of gigajoules (GJ), and the cost of heat is often represented in units of dollars-per-gigajoule ($/GJ). Natural gas is typically priced in units of dollars per 1000 cubic feet ($/mcf), and coal in units of dollars per metric ton ($/mt).

How Much Does Heat Cost?

The two main sources of *carbon-based* heat are natural gas and coal:

- Heat typically costs $3 to $6/GJ when burning $3 to $6/mcf natural gas.
- Heat typically costs $1.5 to $6/GJ when burning $33 to $132/mt coal.

Sources of *green* heat include heat directly from a nuclear reactor and renewables (e.g. solar, wind, hydro):

- Heat direct from a nuclear reactor in China costs approximately $4/GJ and is similar to the cost of burning natural gas. Chinese reactors are often built one at a time. However, if manufactured in larger quantities, their costs would be less.
- High-temperature heat costs $8 to $16/GJ when created with 3¢ to 6¢/kWh green electricity via a direct heating element.

Heat Costs Are Mostly Driven by Fuel Costs

The following tables show the approximate cost of heat from burning natural gas and coal as a function of fuel cost. Also shown is the cost of heat from electricity as a function of electricity cost. As one can see, generating heat with electricity is often not competitive with burning natural gas or coal. The prices shown here are typical for large industrial customers.

	Cost Of Heat	Cost of Fuel	
Burn Natural Gas	Heat ($/GJ)	Heat $/mmbtu	Gas $/mcf
(1.03MMbtu/mcf)	$3.00	$3.17	$3.20
	$4.00	$4.22	$4.26
	$5.00	$5.28	$5.33
	$6.00	$6.34	$6.39

	Cost Of Heat	Cost of Fuel		
Burn Coal	Heat ($/GJ)	Heat $/mmbtu	Coal $/ short ton	Coal $/ metric ton
(21MMbtu/tonne)	$1.50	$1.59	$30	$33
	$3.00	$3.17	$60	$66
	$4.51	$4.76	$90	$99
	$6.01	$6.34	$120	$132
	$8.01	$8.46	$160	$176
	$10.68	$11.28	$213	$235

	Cost Of Heat	Cost of Fuel	
Electricity to Heat	Heat ($/GJ)	Electricity ($/kWh)	Electricity (¢/kWh)
(heating element)	$8.31	$0.03	3¢
	$11.08	$0.04	4¢
	$13.85	$0.05	5¢
	$16.62	$0.06	6¢

Figure 23.3: Cost of heat when burning natural gas, burning coal, and converting electricity directly to heat.

Low Utilization Is Costly

It is costly to underutilize expensive factory equipment; therefore, a persistent energy source, such as a nuclear reactor, is often desired. Unfortunately, solar farms only provide significant power approximately 25% of the time, and wind farms only provide significant power approximately 40% of the time.

Figure 23.4: Industrial equipment is expensive and, therefore, prefers to operate 24 x 7.

Conclusion

In conclusion, high-temperate nuclear reactors in China are the lowest cost sources of green heat in the world. Consequently, nations averse to nuclear power in the future might not be competitive when making green chemicals and green materials.

24. The Economics of Green Fuel

A fuel is a compound that is typically used to (a) store energy, (b) transport energy, (c) produce heat via burning, (d) produce force via expansion, and (e) produce electricity via a fuel cell device. Examples of fuels are coal, gasoline, and natural gas.

To decarbonize, one needs fuels that do not emit CO_2 when made *and* consumed. Examples are hydrogen gas (H_2) and liquid ammonia (NH_3), which are made with green electricity or with heat from a nuclear reactor.

When hydrogen and ammonia are *consumed*, CO_2 is not emitted. And when these are *made* without emitting CO_2, they are referred to as "green." This chapter discusses the lowest cost way of making green fuels.

Co-Locate Nuclear Fission and Manufacturing

One can transfer heat from a nuclear reactor to a heat-driven process less than 1000 meters away via a pipe that carries a hot gas or a hot liquid such as molten salt. One can then use this heat to make things such as hydrogen, ammonia, chemicals, and materials.

Co-locating nuclear reactors with manufacturing is typically not done; however, this might change due to cost. In other words, a nation that co-locates fission with hydrogen and ammonia production might dominate these markets due to lower costs. An illustration of this is shown below.

Figure 24.1: Illustration of nuclear reactor co-located with high-temperature manufacturing (Source: Idaho National Laboratory).

Why Hydrogen and Ammonia Are Important

A hydrocarbon is a type of fuel that only contains hydrogen (H) and carbon (C) atoms. Examples are oil, gasoline, and natural gas. When these burn, their carbon atoms bond with oxygen (O) from the atmosphere and form CO_2, a greenhouse gas. Subsequently, if one wants something that burns and does not emit CO_2, one needs a compound that does not contain carbon (C), such as hydrogen gas (H_2) or liquid ammonia (NH_3).

An "energy carrier" is a substance that transports energy from one place to another. The four big carriers of green energy are green electricity, piped green hydrogen gas, green liquid ammonia, and green heat in a pipe (e.g. steam or molten salt). To produce green energy carriers, one needs an energy source that does not emit CO_2, such as wind, solar, hydro, or nuclear power.

Hydrogen gas moves easily in a pipe, provided one has a pipe. However, it does not transport in a vehicle easily. Nor does it store easily due to its 700 atm (10,000 psi) pressure when compressed as a gas in a tank at room temperature, or its -253°C (-423°F) temperature when a liquid not under pressure. Electricity in large quantities does not store easily either. Therefore, if one wants low-cost green storage or low-cost transportation via truck, train, or ship, one might be looking at tanked liquid ammonia.

Ammonia is NH_3, which means it is three hydrogen atoms with one nitrogen atom. Adding and subtracting nitrogen atoms to and from hydrogen consumes energy and costs money. However, it is sometimes worth the effort due to easier storage and transportation.

Ammonia can be: (a) burned directly after being mixed with something more flammable, (b) turned into hydrogen after removing its nitrogen atom, or (c) pushed into an ammonia fuel cell to make electricity.

Liquid ammonia in a tank needs to be refrigerated to -33°C (-27°F) if under no pressure, or pressurized to 10 atm (150 psi) pressure if at room temperature. This is cumbersome; however, the world has much experience with ammonia since it is used to make fertilizer.

Figure 24.3: A rail tank car being filled with liquid ammonia.

In summary, green energy involves sources, carriers, and storage:

Green Energy *Sources:* Solar panels, hydroelectric dams, windmills, and nuclear power plants.

Green Energy *Carriers:* Green electricity traveling in a wire, green heat traveling as steam in a pipe, green hydrogen gas traveling in a pipe, and green liquid ammonia traveling in a pipe.

Green Energy *Storage:* Green liquid ammonia in a tank, green electricity in a battery, and hot molten salt in a tank.

Lowest Cost Green Hydrogen and Ammonia

If one converts one gigawatt (1 GW_h) of hot heat to hydrogen via a 56% efficient low-cost process (e.g. sulfur-iodine via nuclear reactor heat), one will get 0.56GW of cheap hydrogen. Alternatively, if one converts heat to electricity with a 42% efficient electrical turbine and converts electricity to hydrogen with a costly ~80% efficient process, they will get 0.33GW of costly hydrogen (42% x 80%). In other words, when making hydrogen, hot green heat (e.g. nuclear reactor) costs less than hot electricity (e.g. high-temperature electrolysis via nuclear reactor), and hot electricity costs less than cold electricity (e.g. low-temperature electrolysis via solar/wind/hydro).

After making hydrogen (H_2), one can add a nitrogen atom to make ammonia (NH_3) and then transport it to any location. Later, the ammonia can be converted to hydrogen by removing the nitrogen atom, or the ammonia can be fed into an ammonia fuel cell to produce electricity.

Nuclear reactors in China cost three times less than nuclear reactors in the U.S. or Europe. Therefore, the lowest-cost way to make green hydrogen and green ammonia is probably a chemical process driven by heat from a nuclear reactor in China.

Figure 24.4: Nuclear power plant.

Why Is Lowest Cost Important?

Costs are important since consumers buy the lowest cost product, independent of where it is made or how it is made. In other words, if the lowest cost is made with China nuclear, consumers will buy it, even if they do not like China and do not like nuclear. This is consistent with economic theory and observed behavior.

A high-temperature fission reactor might produce 700°C; however, many processes need higher temperatures. For example, curing cement requires ~1400°C. The lowest-cost way to go higher is probably to pre-heat to 700°C with direct nuclear reactor heat and then go higher by burning green hydrogen.

Advanced reactors, such as HTR-PM in China, have uranium-based nuclear fuel that reduces energy output when nuclear fuel temperature exceeds normal operation, to the extent required to avoid melting when not cooled. In other words, newer and more advanced nuclear fission reactors are significantly safer than older reactors.

Fuel Costs

Energy is often represented in units of gigajoules (GJ), and energy costs are often represented in units of dollars-per-gigajoule ($/GJ). Fuels can be converted to heat by burning (i.e. "combustion"). Therefore, one can think of their cost as the number of dollars needed to produce one gigajoule of heat when they are burned.

The upper third of the following table shows the wholesale cost of existing carbon-based fuels. We are working with pre-COVID prices since they were more stable.

Type	Fuel	$/GJ	Cost	Conditions
Carbon-Based Fuel, USA, 2019	Gasoline	$16.38	$2.12/gal	USA, Wholesale, 2019, Pre-COVID
	Diesel	$14.37	$2.1/gal	"
	Ethanol	$25.76	$2.34/gal	"
	Crude Oil	$8.97	$1.25/gal	"
	Heating Oil	$12.75	$1.8/gal	"
	Natural Gas	$3.19	$3.4/mcf	"
	Coal, Anthracite	$2.09	$57/ton	"
	Electricity from Natural Gas	$11.11	$0.04/kWh	Electricity made with natural gas, USA, 2019
Green Energy Inside China	Green Heat, China, Nuclear*	$3.99	$4.21/mmbtu	Made with HTR-PM nuclear reactor ($2400/kW) in China, consumed ≤ 1000 meters from reactor
	Green Hydrogen, China, Nuclear*	$8.93	$1.26/kg	Made w/ HTR-PM nuclear reactor in China, delivered to China via pipe, sulfur-iodine (56%, $500/kW)
	Green Electricity, China, Nuclear*	$9.51	$0.034/kWh	Made w/ HTR-PM nuclear reactor in China, 24 x 365, 42% efficient turbine
Green Energy Outside China	Green Ammonia, Any Location*	$15.24	$0.66/gal	Made w/ HTR-PM nuclear reactor in China, delivered to any location via ship, Haber-Bosch (65%, $300/kW)
	Green Hydrogen, Any Location*	$18.29	$2.58/kg	Ammonia made w/ HTR-PM reactor in China, shipped to any location, and then converted to hydrogen.
	Green Electricity, Solar/Wind	$10.46	$0.038/kWh	PV Solar (25% availability) or land-based wind power (40% availablity).

*Still in development, cost is estimate

Figure 24.5: Estimated cost of select fuels in units of wholesale dollars-per-gigajoule (Calculations by Weinreb).

The middle third of the table estimates the cost of green energy made with nuclear fission power in China. This includes heat directly from the reactor, green hydrogen made by the reactor, and green ammonia made by the reactor. Manufacturing via direct nuclear reactor heat is still in development; therefore, these costs are estimated.

The lower third of the table estimates costs after green ammonia has been transported from China to any location. As discussed previously, ammonia can be consumed directly, converted to hydrogen, or converted to electricity. Also shown is the typical cost of electricity made by solar, wind, or hydroelectric power.

Fuel Reflections

Below are several comments based on the above data.

- The cost of heat directly from a nuclear reactor in China is similar to the cost of heat from burning natural gas or coal.

- Burning piped green hydrogen gas in China is not competitive with burning natural gas or coal in China.

- Green hydrogen gas outside China, made with green ammonia from China, is not competitive with burning gas or coal outside China.

- Green ammonia from China could be used to make electricity at any location via several different methods; however, this is not competitive with electricity from solar, wind, or hydroelectric power.

- Outside China, the cost of gasoline is similar to the cost of green ammonia made with China's nuclear reactors. Moreover, ammonia fuel cells that convert ammonia to electricity are typically twice as efficient as gasoline internal combustion engines. Therefore, green ammonia made in China could potentially compete with gasoline and diesel fuel outside of China. For details, see *How to Decarbonize Transportation* *(Power Electronics, Oct 2021)*.

Conclusion

In the future, green hydrogen gas and green liquid ammonia will probably be as important as today's natural gas and oil. Nuclear reactors are the lowest-cost way to make these green fuels. Therefore, nations will probably either: (a) import green fuel or (b) make green fuel locally after improving nuclear fission safety and reducing its cost.

25. High-Temperature Green Manufacturing at the Lowest Cost

This chapter discusses how one might decarbonize high-temperature green manufacturing at the lowest cost. This includes making green chemicals (e.g. hydrogen, ammonia) and green materials (e.g. plastics, metals, ceramics, glass, cement).

What to Do If Your Competitor's Factory Costs $0

Reports often compare the cost of a green product with its carbon-based counterpart when both production factories are built from scratch. However, this typically does not occur when decarbonizing. Instead, the carbon-based factory is already built and paid for. And one would like the new green factory to cost less than the incremental cost of operating the old factory. In most cases, new green fails economically against existing carbon. This is one reason why economists' predictions about CO_2 are so dour.

It would be helpful if new laws required decarbonization, with additional costs passed onto consumers. However, the public is not comfortable with these at this time. To press forward, one might look at cost reduction via automation and standardization, both in factories and the field. Climate change entails building trillions of dollars of infrastructure; therefore, it is reasonable to spend billions on R&D to save trillions. Yet what might one develop? And how might one initially spend tens of millions of dollars *before* spending billions?

Green Manufacturing *at Lowest Cost*

As discussed previously, the lowest cost way to do high-temperature green manufacturing is probably to pump a hot working fluid from a nuclear fission reactor to nearby industrial processes, as illustrated in the previous chapter's first figure. This is not being done today; however, it could be done in the future.

The cost-per-gigajoule of green hydrogen made with a nuclear reactor would probably be 2 to 3-times higher than the cost-per-gigajoule of direct heat from the reactor. Therefore, nearby heat-driven industrial processes might utilize direct reactor heat, while faraway processes on the same continent might utilize piped green hydrogen gas.

Nuclear power is 3-times less costly in China than in the U.S. and Europe. And China is building nuclear reactors at a fast pace; therefore, the above concept would most likely appear first in China. However, a decarbonization laboratory outside of China might be inclined to work on nuclear heat-based manufacturing, to reduce global CO_2 emissions.

Industrial Processing *at Lowest Cost*

The photograph below shows industrial processing equipment that was built in a factory-like shipyard and placed onto a floating platform. This costs less than assembling in the field, especially if the factory is in China and the field is in Europe or the U.S.

Figure 25.1: Ship-mounted industrial processing equipment.

Moving Super-Sized Equipment from Factory to Site

Currently, there is no way to move ship-sized industrial processing equipment from a factory to a site. However, if we are looking for R&D to reduce the cost of green manufacturing, this might be a good time to explore new transportation systems, an example of which is illustrated below.

Figure 25.2: Super-sized 12 x 24m railcar (Concept illustration by Weinreb).

In this concept, 12m by 24m railcars are mounted on double tracks 12m apart. These roll from the factory or shipyard to the dock at the water's edge, to the ship, to the dock near the site, and then to the site. The distance between the factory and the water, and from the water to the site, might be less than 10km (16miles) since this involves special track.

In some cases, one might rip up short segments of an existing track and rebuild with a total of four tracks, two for existing trains, and two for extra-wide railcars, as illustrated below. Alternatively, one might have two tracks instead of four and use the same track for both local and wide traffic. However, this would require both sets to use the same rail gauge.

Figure 25.3: Traditional rail co-located with extra-wide rail.

Rolling between ship and shore is not new, as shown below. Ballast tanks align the height of the ship to the height of the shore.

Figure 25.4: Railcars transported by ship.

The illustrations below show how one might: (i) transport eight standard-sized containers on one railcar, (ii) transport 2-wide, 3-wide or 4-wide containers, (iii) transport bulk material such as iron ore in a bin, and (iv) transport equipment on a flat steel plate.

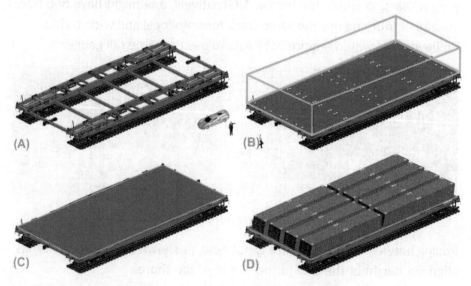

Figure 25.5: Super-sized railcar supports standard-sized containers (Concept illustration by Weinreb).

A new transportation system that moves large and heavy objects would probably have a significant impact on industrial site design, manufacturing strategy, and total site cost. Also, an initial paper-only design would be relatively easy because rail, ship, and crane technology already exists.

Moving Large Platforms

The equipment on the ship in the above photograph is larger than one railcar. Therefore, engineers might place a truss on top of multiple rail cars, as illustrated below. In this concept, jacks between railcars and truss keep truss straight as train bends side-to-side and up-and-down. To get a sense of size, note the person in the lower-left corner.

Figure 25.6: Large platform of equipment transported on long straight truss (Concept illustration by Weinreb).

Standardized Site

If we extend this further, the platforms eventually plug into a site, as shown below. In this concept illustration, multiple nuclear reactors provide heat (center) to 25 platforms of equipment (upper-left corner). Each platform might be on the order of 12m x 96m. Standards define how platforms communicate, connect mechanically and connect electrically. Site-wide efficiency is maximized by capturing unused heat and redirecting it to make electricity, make chemicals, and increase the temperature of thermal storage.

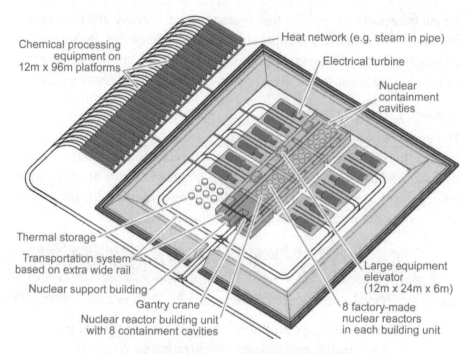

Chemical processing
equipment on
12m x 96m platforms

Heat network (e.g. steam in pipe)

Electrical turbine

Nuclear
containment
cavities

Thermal storage

Transportation system
based on extra wide rail

Nuclear support building

Gantry crane

Nuclear reactor building unit
with 8 containment cavities

Large equipment
elevator
(12m x 24m x 6m)

8 factory-made
nuclear reactors
in each building unit

Figure 25.7: High-temperature standardized
green manufacturing site (Concept illustration by Weinreb).

Factory-Made Nuclear Reactors

Nuclear power in the U.S. and Europe is costly. However, if nuclear reactor equipment was mass-produced in a factory, it would cost less. If one extends the super-sized railcar concept further, one might envision a building that houses factory-made nuclear reactors that are transported by large railcar, as illustrated below. For details, see *How to Reduce the Cost of Nuclear Fission Power*.

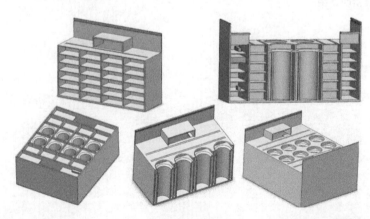

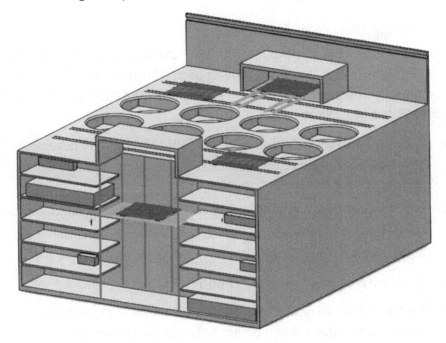

Figure 25.8: Building contains factory-made nuclear reactor equipment transported via extra-wide rail (Concept by Weinreb).

Balancing Load and Recovering Waste Heat

If a nuclear reactor is used to make electricity, make hydrogen gas, and power heat-driven industrial processes, then tanks of molten salt could potentially help to balance loads. For example, if electricity demand was low, reactor heat could be stored in tanks of molten salt and used later when electricity demand was especially high.

Many industrial processes produce waste heat that is lost to the atmosphere. One would prefer to use it in some way; however, it is rarely at a convenient temperature and power level. For example, curing cement might need 1400°C at 10MJ/sec, while waste heat after generating electricity might be different. Tanks of molten salt could potentially help to synchronize multiple processes when using waste heat.

To reduce the cost of molten salt storage tanks, engineers could explore: (a) placing extra-wide rail next to tanks, (b) fabricating tank components in factories and transporting via extra-wide rail, and (c) automating tank assembly via machines mounted on extra-wide railcars.

How Might R&D Push This Forward?

Investment capital would probably consider the above concepts "too big," "too much risk," and "too many moving parts." The truth is, they are. If one component is missing, revenue is zero. How might R&D push this forward? Below is one possible approach.

- A government or foundation budgets $10M to $100M to develop next-generation high-temperature green manufacturing sites, standards, and supporting transportation infrastructure.

- The initiative supports multiple paper-only designs, simulations, simple prototypes of components, and proposals for more work. However, an actual site is not built. For that, one needs more money.

- Heat sources include nuclear fission/fusion and concentrated solar.

- Engineers explore new transportation systems that move large platforms of industrial equipment between factory and site.

- Standards are developed that define how equipment connects mechanically, electrically, and in software.

- All scientists and engineers who receive money are required to make produced materials open source (e.g. software, designs, simulations, etc). Subsequently, anyone can view, copy, and modify at no cost.

- Transparency and open source are required since this is too big for one organization to build themselves. And companies typically cannot afford to develop interconnection standards used mostly by others.

Conclusion

High-temperature green manufacturing is unlikely to decarbonize anytime soon without aggressive cost reduction. And this would require billions of dollars of R&D. A foundation or government could potentially get started for less money. However, this would require a visionary leader who is willing to tackle large next-generation systems. Someone like Elon Musk might be a good fit; however, he is busy trying to leave the planet. In conclusion, we need a new generation of leaders who are willing to rethink next-generation green manufacturing.

26. Transportation is a 30 Trillion Dollar Problem

U.S. government engineers at EIA expect CO_2 emissions from U.S. transportation to remain approximately constant over the next 30 years, as shown below. In other words, according to the U.S. government, the U.S. is not decarbonizing transportation.

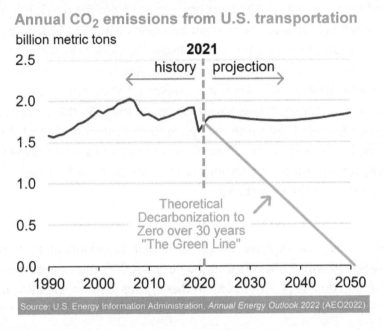

Figure 26.1: Projected annual CO_2 emissions from U.S. transportation.

As noted previously, consumers go green if required by law or if the green option costs less. And EIA does not expect either with transportation. This is partly due to challenges involving: (a) rare earth materials, (b) fast-charging, and (c) grid decarbonization.

Decarbonizing Transportation for Real

A green line in the above graph shows what it would look like to decarbonize transportation over 30 years. To do this line, at least one of the following would need to occur: (i) reduce the cost of green cars to below that of gas cars via more R&D, more productive EV manufacturing, or more government subsidies, (ii) enact laws that require consumers buy green cars even if they cost more, or (iii) enact laws that allow cheap EVs to enter domestic markets. Also, if transportation is powered by electricity, the grid needs to be decarbonized.

U.S. Transportation Legislation

In 2010 the U.S. set up a program to reduce the effective cost of electric vehicles by contributing approximately $7.5K to each EV sold. For example, if the EV sells for $40K, the U.S. federal government pays $7.5K via reduced tax, and the buyer pays $32.5K. As one can see from the previous graph, this resulted in Mild Decarbonization between 2010 and 2021. To do the Transportation Green Line for real via legislation, one would need significantly more government intervention. And this would probably require a coalition of lawmakers from regions that do not produce oil and do not manufacture gasoline-powered cars. In the U.S., there are not enough Democrats from these regions to form a majority. Therefore, one would probably need support from Green Republicans. And they would probably require simple legislation that focuses on decarbonizing transportation at the lowest cost.

Real Transportation Decarbonization via More R&D

There are 1,500,000,000 gas cars (1.5 billion) in the world, and if these were replaced with $20K cars that did not emit CO_2, the total cost would be 30 trillion dollars (1.5B x $20K). In theory, this justifies spending billions of additional dollars on R&D to make green cars cost less than gas cars.

Consider HEV for Quick Improvement

If one is looking to reduce CO_2 emissions quickly without spending money, consider government intervention that encourages gasoline and diesel-powered cars to include a tiny electric motor that improves fuel mileage by approximately 30%. This adds ~$1.5K to the initial price of the car; however, this additional cost is paid back within one to three years due to savings at the gas station.

Gas cars with tiny electric motors are referred to as "Hybrid Electric Vehicles" (HEV) and are often misunderstood due to having a name similar to "Plugin Hybrid Electric Vehicle" (PHEV). The plug-in cost ~$12K more than the gas car and has a large electric motor that enables it to run exclusively on electricity for ~40 miles. Alternatively, the non-plugin HEV has a regular-sized gasoline engine. And it has a tiny electric motor and a tiny battery that recovers energy while braking and pushes the car while coasting. Most of the time, cars do not accelerate, and a tiny electric motor (e.g. 20hp) can maintain a constant speed.

In theory, government could require this tiny electric motor to be added to gasoline engines. Or it could require improved gasoline mileage, which can be achieved with this additional hardware. For details, see *How to Improve Gas Mileage 25% to 50% (Power Electronics, Aug 2022).*

Car Lifetime Costs

A vehicle's lifetime cost is the sum of the following components: (a) initial vehicle cost, (b) replacement battery cost, (c) repair cost, and (d) gasoline or electricity fuel cost. The typical car lasts 200K miles; therefore, one can divide lifetime cost by 200K miles to calculate the average cost-per-mile over a lifetime.

Most EV batteries are warrantied for 100K miles; therefore, one can expect to replace the battery at least once during a vehicle's 200K mile lifetime (100K x 2). Batteries typically cost $15K, and it is not clear how their costs will change over time since battery materials might become rarer and more costly as consumption increases.

EVs Cost less than Gas Cars When Gasoline Is Expensive

If the price of gasoline is high and the price of electricity is low, the lifetime cost of an EV could potentially be less than that of a gas car. Gasoline prices surged in 2022, and this caused EV sales to also surge. However, gasoline is not expected to stay high forever, as noted by EIA's graph at the beginning of this chapter.

It is easy to think the next 30 years will be similar to this year, and fuel prices will not change appreciably. However, government economists do not see it that way. Instead, they expect fuel prices to decrease when fuel production increases, or economic activity decreases.

The table below calculates the lifetime cost for both the Hyundai Kona electric vehicle and the same model with a gasoline engine. Also, it makes this comparison with different gasoline and electricity prices. As one can see, the EV costs less than the gasoline car when gasoline prices are high.

For details, see *Car Costs and CO$_2$ are Complicated* (Power Electronics, Sept 2022).

Gas Cost ($/gal)	Electricity Cost ($/kWh)	Kona Gas Car Lifetime $	Kona EV Lifetime ($)	Difference ($)	EV Cost Less with 100K mi battery?	EV Cost Less with 200K mi battery?
$2.00	$ 0.10	$35,408	$52,681	$17,274	no	no
$3.00	$ 0.10	$41,562	$52,681	$11,120	no	yes
$4.00	$ 0.10	$47,715	$52,681	$4,966	no	yes
$5.00	$ 0.10	$53,869	$52,681	-$1,188	yes	yes
$6.00	$ 0.10	$60,023	$52,681	-$7,342	yes	yes
$7.00	$ 0.10	$66,177	$52,681	-$13,496	yes	yes
$2.00	$ 0.20	$35,408	$57,642	$22,235	no	no
$3.00	$ 0.20	$41,562	$57,642	$16,081	no	no
$4.00	$ 0.20	$47,715	$57,642	$9,927	no	yes
$5.00	$ 0.20	$53,869	$57,642	$3,773	no	yes
$6.00	$ 0.20	$60,023	$57,642	-$2,381	yes	yes
$7.00	$ 0.20	$66,177	$57,642	-$8,534	yes	yes
$2.00	$ 0.30	$35,408	$62,604	$27,196	no	no
$3.00	$ 0.30	$41,562	$62,604	$21,042	no	no
$4.00	$ 0.30	$47,715	$62,604	$14,888	no	no
$5.00	$ 0.30	$53,869	$62,604	$8,734	no	yes
$6.00	$ 0.30	$60,023	$62,604	$2,581	no	yes
$7.00	$ 0.30	$66,177	$62,604	-$3,573	yes	yes

* Conditions: 200K lifetime miles, $13K battery replacement cost, $23K gas car cost, $34K EV cost.

Figure 26.2: Lifetime cost comparison of gas vs. EV, with different gasoline and electricity prices (Calculations by Weinreb).

Double the Lifetime of the EV Battery

Normally, EV batteries are warrantied for 100K miles and are replaced once during a vehicle's 200K mile lifetime. If battery longevity was instead twice as long, and replacement did not occur, EV lifetime costs would decrease significantly.

The second to the last column in the above table assumes the typical 100K mile battery is replaced once, and the last column assumes a 200K mile battery is not replaced. As of this writing, 200K mile batteries do not exist. As one can see, doubling battery longevity via R&D causes EVs to cost less than gas cars in the typical fuel price case. In other words, the easiest way to decarbonize transportation is probably to double the longevity of the battery. For details on how this might work, see *The Little Secret of Electric Vehicles* (Power Electronics, Sept 2022).

Battery Fundamentals

There are different types of batteries, and one can characterize each type with several parameters. These include: (a) cost per unit energy stored, (b) amount of energy stored per unit weight, (c) number of charge/discharge cycles over a battery lifetime, and (d) fastest charging speed.

If one decreases energy stored per weight by a factor of two, and decreases the fastest charging speed by a factor of 16, then battery-system costs are likely to decrease by a factor of three or more. For example, a battery-system that supports a 125-mile (200km) range and an 8-hour fastest charging speed is likely to cost at least 3-times less than a 250-mile (400km) system that supports 30-minute charging.

There are several reasons for this cost reduction, including a 16-fold decrease in power while charging, a 16-fold decrease in heat generated while charging, and a lower-cost battery chemistry.

Half the Car for Half the Money ("Cheap Green Car")

Currently, low-range EVs (e.g. ≤ 125 miles) are sold in the U.S. for $30K (e.g. MINI Electric Cooper) and are sold in China for $12K. These do not sell well in the U.S. since Americans are not comfortable paying $30K for half a car. However, they might pay $15K for half a car. At the right price, U.S. families with two cars might consider having one powerful car and one light electric. And individuals who rarely drive long distances might consider owning a light electric and borrowing more car as needed.

In theory, a nation could define a new automobile class, perhaps called the "Light Electric," and allow low-cost models to enter domestic markets. For example, it might have ≤ 125-mile range, ≥ 8 hours to fully charge, and ≤ 85 mph maximum speed. Alternatively, one might allow all automobile classes to enter domestic markets; however, lawmakers might consider that too disruptive. To push cheap green car forward, one would probably need a coalition of lawmakers from regions that do not produce cars or gas.

The Charging Problem

Over the last few years, what did you see when glancing at fast charging stations? Did you see cars charging? In many cases, fast charging stations are underutilized.

Figure 26.3 Charging stations are often underutilized.

The equipment cost-per-charge is determined by the equipment cost divided by the number of charges. Therefore, the cost-per-charge is high when the number of charges is low. This causes fast charging to typically cost three times more than slow charging at home. This, along with charging inconvenience, causes EV owners to rarely fast charge.

The greatest challenge with fast charging cannot be seen. It is electricity. The typical 50kWh EV battery consumes 100kW of power when charging in 30 minutes (100kW x 0.5h). This is the same amount of power drawn by 80 U.S. homes on average. In other words, supporting large amounts of power is expensive, especially if the hardware is underutilized.

Charging stations are often located at shopping malls and hotels since they have plenty of power for air conditioning. This power can be redirected when the air conditioning is off. However, one still needs expensive electronics to convert grid AC power to battery DC power. And to reduce cost, this gear is often undersized. This leads to longer charging times, especially when multiple cars are charging at the same time. And this leads to more range anxiety since drivers often do not know how long it will take to charge since it depends on who else is charging, and air conditioning.

Swappable Battery

There is one way to resolve all of the problems alluded to in this chapter. It is a standardized plug-in swappable EV battery. Currently, the world has mechanical and electrical standards that define batteries, and these enable us to power many products at a low cost.

Figure 26.4: Examples of standardized batteries.

In theory, one could have a standardized car battery that looks similar to the Tesla EV battery yet is used by multiple manufacturers. The standard would define the mechanics (e.g., height, length, and width), electrical connections, and communication between battery and car. This is not a new idea. For a <u>video</u> that discusses this, search "2-xwyscsvts" on YouTube.

Currently, proprietary batteries are built into EVs and are charged periodically. Alternatively, one could have a standard plug-in battery, wherein all cars use the same form, and swap with a fresh battery in less than one minute. Car owners would pay for electricity consumed and wear on the battery. And they would be charged less when using lower-range lower-cost batteries. Cavities would be dug out at key locations, and a mechanism that charges, stores, and swaps would be dropped in. Cars would position themselves over the mechanism and swap.

Figure 26.5: EV batteries are typically placed low and between wheels to reduce the risk of rolling over due to a high center of gravity.

Those who drive less than 100 miles (160 km) per day could swap in a low-cost, low-range battery and charge at night. Cost reduction would occur because lower-range batteries use fewer rare Earth materials. For long trips, one could swap in a costly high-range battery or swap more often. Swapping would also reduce costs via commoditization since multiple battery manufacturers would compete and drive down the price.

Homes could install swap chambers in their driveway with multiple batteries, as illustrated below. These could be charged by solar panels during the day, power the house at night, and swap with cars as needed.

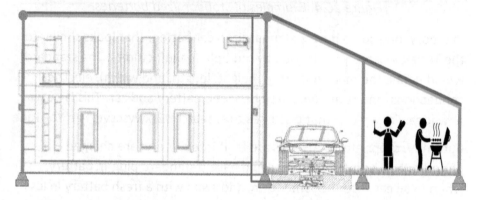

Figure 26.6: EV batteries in swap chamber power homes at night (Concept illustration by Weinreb).

The downside is that swap would require a massive effort by automakers who would need to design vehicles around a swappable battery and construct new factories to make those vehicles. And the world would need to install millions of swap chambers at great cost.

To move this forward, a government or foundation could spend $10M to $100M to develop an open-source standardized swappable battery system to the point of simple prototypes. For details, see *Are we Ready for a Swappable EV Battery? (Power Electronics, Aug 2022).*

Ammonia Based Transportation

In theory, vehicles could be powered by liquid ammonia. However, making this work economically and technically would require billions of dollars of R&D. The car is the tip of the iceberg since the entire fuel supply chain is what determines the total cost. The entire system would need to be economically competitive with gasoline-based transportation in order for it to be accepted globally. This is theoretically possible via (a) green ammonia made with nuclear reactors in regions that are receptive to nuclear power,

(b) fuel cells in vehicles that convert ammonia to electricity for motors, (c) automated refueling infrastructure that supports transferring multiple chemicals into and out of the vehicle, and (d) emergency response systems that handle ammonia failures.

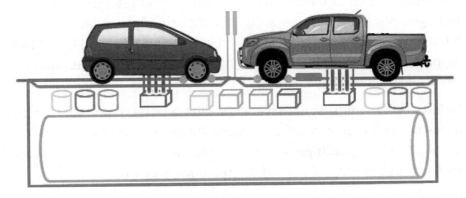

Figure 26.7: Automated refueling (Concept illustration by Weinreb)

As discussed in the previous "Economics of Green Fuel" chapter, ammonia made with nuclear reactors in China is likely to cost approximately $15 per gigajoule of energy, and gasoline often costs more. And fuel cells are typically more efficient than internal combustion engines. In other words, ammonia-based transportation, cheaper than gas, is theoretically possible.

This might seem complicated, and it is. Also, battery-powered EVs is just as complicated, if not more so. Battery-powered EVs need to deal with decarbonizing the grid, the cost of rare earth materials as consumption increases, charging station economic viability, reducing EV costs below that of gasoline-based transportation, and providing convenience comparable to gasoline. And, as noted at the beginning of this chapter, engineers at EIA do not expect these challenges to be overcome.

In theory, a division within a decarbonization laboratory could be tasked with designing a global system that powers transportation with ammonia at the lowest cost and cheaper than gasoline. With a relatively small budget, one could do paper-only designs and build simple prototypes. For details, see *How to Decarbonize Transportation (Power Electronics, Oct 2021).*

Hydrogen Based Transportation

One could also have a division within a decarbonization laboratory that does the same with hydrogen gas-based transportation.

If a country like China created hydrogen with nuclear reactors and fed the hydrogen into a pipe network within Asia they could power factories, heat buildings, and power vehicles. The hydrogen (H_2) would probably cost half as much as ammonia (NH_3) since adding and subtracting nitrogen atoms (N) to and from hydrogen (H) costs money.

Unfortunately, hydrogen has several disadvantages: (a) it probably requires a pipe network to be economically viable, (b) pipes do not easily cross oceans, (c) storing hydrogen in tanks is expensive, and (d) making hydrogen with renewables (e.g. solar, wind, hydro) tends to be expensive.

Consumers buy the lowest-cost product. For example, if the lowest cost is made with a nuclear reactor in China, consumers will buy it even if they do not like nuclear and China. For this reason, engineers who design a global ammonia or hydrogen-based transportation system would need to identify the lowest-cost approach in order for their work to be relevant.

Transportation R&D

One can decarbonize via brute-force or via R&D. The latter typically costs less. However, it is often not clear what, where, and how to develop. A decarbonization laboratory with a transportation division could potentially be helpful. Groups within the division might include: (a) design global well-to-wheels lowest-cost ammonia-based transportation system, (b) same but with hydrogen, (c) develop a swappable battery standard, (d) increase battery longevity to beyond the lifespan of the car ("kill the replacement battery"), (e) study light electric vehicle category ("half the car for half the money"), and (f) study requiring small electric motors in gasoline-based cars.

27. The National Solar Farm (proposed)

Approximately 3% of U.S. electricity is generated by solar farms, and this only increases by 0.5% each year. Unfortunately, this growth rate would need to be much higher if one wanted to decarbonize the U.S. within a reasonable period. Yet how might one increase this rate? Could one automate solar farm financing, construction, and maintenance with software?

We will explore these questions and discuss a potential concept which we will refer to as the "National Solar Farm System" (NSFS). This does not exist. However, it could exist, perhaps after one to three years of software development. In summary, the NSFS would oversee solar farm owners, investors, and customers.

- **Owners** build and maintain solar farms.
- **Investors** pay for solar farm construction in return for a portion of electricity revenue.
- **Customers** buy electricity generated by solar farms.

Participation in NSFS would be optional. In other words, solar farm owners would either operate traditionally or within NSFS.

Figure 27.1: Large solar farm.

Solar Bonds

When a government builds a highway for automobiles, it typically: (a) issues bonds to fund construction, (b) uses toll revenue to pay bond holders, and (c) allows bonds to be traded. The value of a bond is typically the sum of its expected future payments, discounted by inflation. A national solar farm system would be similar. The initial bond would pay for solar farm construction, electricity revenue would support dividend payments to bond-holders, and bonds could be traded.

Figure 27.2: Illustration of solar bond. This is not a real product.

Individuals would register at a website, transfer money to their account, buy solar capacity within the system, receive money based on electricity sales, and sell solar capacity with the click of a mouse.

Each share would be referred to as a "solar bond," and each bond would be economically equivalent to a 300W solar panel. Therefore, each bond would cost $336 if solar farm parts and labor construction cost were $1.12-per-watt ($1.12 x 300W).

Financial Requirements

To get this to work economically, the system would need to meet the following requirements:

• The rate of return to investors would need to be similar to or greater than that offered by traditional bonds for the same level of risk. In other words, investors would not participate if solar bonds were not competitive with other investment opportunities.

- Electricity would need to be priced at its cost plus a reasonable profit to the solar farm owner. Otherwise, if the electricity price were too high, electricity customers would seek alternatives. And if too low, solar farm owners would not participate.

The Tension between Investors and Customers

The green option often costs more than the carbon-based option. Therefore, to decarbonize, government subsidies need to close the gap, or new laws need to require customers to buy green and pay a higher price. As noted previously, the price difference between the green option and the carbon option is commonly referred to as the "green premium."

Both investors and electricity customers need to be kept happy; otherwise, neither will participate. A dollar saved by the electricity customer is approximately one dollar less received by the investor. Therefore, to get this to work economically, competition among solar farm owners would need to drive down costs and drive down electricity price, and investors would need to see a competitive return on their investment.

Risk Is as Important as Price

What is the probability that a solar farm owner buys junky hardware, promises a low price due to lower costs, and has the hardware fail prematurely? The result would be reduced dividends to investors due to less electricity revenue. Yet, more importantly, other investors would see this and be less likely to participate in future NSFS projects.

What is the probability that an owner promises a low electricity price to be competitive and uses money from future projects to pay for past projects? This is referred to as "Ponzi."

Unfortunately, the probability of these problems is high unless a mechanism is in place that blocks each. Suppose one has a market with 100 suppliers, and 10 of them are Ponzi or favor junk, either wittingly or unwittingly. The 10 are more likely to win contracts due to quoting lower prices or quoting higher returns to investors. In some markets, the honest and competent engineer finishes last. In other words, the risk of Ponzi and the risk of junk need to be controlled.

Transparency Enables One to Control Risk

The enemy of Ponzi and the enemy of junk is transparency. If all information is disclosed, risk and returns can be calculated more accurately.

There are two types of transparency, technical and economic. Technical entails publicly reporting solar farm design, lists of components, amount of electricity produced, solar panel efficiency vs. time, and technical failures. Economic transparency entails publicly reporting equipment costs, maintenance costs, and electricity revenue.

To get the NSFS to work economically, at large scales, it might need to be transparent. In other words, designs with known performance might need to be made public, so that they can be easily copied and improved.

The probability that an investment fails is referred to as "risk." And if one can reduce risk, one can reduce the rate of return demanded by investors and therefore reduce the price paid by electricity customers. In other words, risk is somewhat proportional to electricity price. If risk goes down, electricity price goes down too. Also, transparency reduces risk. Therefore, transparency reduces electricity price.

Some solar farm owners might be uncomfortable with transparency and avoid NSFS. However, others might find it acceptable, especially if they can copy what works, have it perform as expected, and easily access capital.

Investors might favor NSFS over traditional options due to transparency and additional oversite. However, NSFS would be unpopular if it did not function properly for a variety of reasons, such as buggy software.

Solar Farms within the System

The NSFS oversees multiple solar farms, each of which has an owner and one or more customers. Before a solar farm is built, the owner would submit an application that includes a technical plan and an economic plan. The technical plan would include the technical design and list of components. And the economic plan would include expected equipment costs, maintenance costs, etc. Owners could copy proposals from existing solar farms or expand existing farms. The NSFS organization would estimate risk, estimate the cost of capital, and introduce electricity customers to farm owners. Projects would not be funded unless the owner had a customer that agreed to an electricity price.

The NSFS organization would take care of financing by selling bonds through an automated system. To diversify risk, multiple solar farms would be put together into one bond issue. In other words, a bond-holder might own a small piece of dozens of solar farms. Subsequently, if one farm failed, consequences would be minimized. The NSFS computer would keep track of revenue from each farm and calculate who gets what.

The Solar Commissioner

The system would be overseen by a Solar Commissioner whose first priority would be to represent the interests of the government, second priority would be to represent the interests of investors, and third priority would be to represent the interests of electricity customers.

As mentioned previously, government wants a decent number of solar farms constructed each year, investors want to maximize their return on investment (for a given level of risk), electricity customers want to minimize price, and solar farm owners want to maximize profit.

The NSFS would oversee the following kind of process:

1. Government sets the minimum amount of solar farm capacity built each year.

2. Commissioner sets investment rate-of-return, for a given level of risk, sufficient to the raise money needed for step #1.

3. Commissioner gathers proposals from potential owners to build solar farms.

4. Commissioner estimates a variety of parameters, such as risk and investor rate-of-return, for each proposal.

5. Commissioner helps establish electricity purchase agreements between solar farm owners and wholesale electricity customers.

6. Commissioner sells solar bonds to pay for new construction.

7. The NSFS computers monitor performance, failures, electricity generated, and revenue.

Calculating expected risk (i.e. probability of economic failure) and expected rate-of-return (i.e. dividend as a percentage of initial investment) requires computers, software, and past data. This is complicated and would therefore need to be handled by an office that reports to the commissioner. If the actual rate of return was less than expected, future investors would be less likely to participate. In other words, calculating accurately would be crucial.

Wind Too

A sister system for wind farms could be built as well. In theory, an automated National Wind Farm System (NWFS) could be overseen by a Wind Commissioner who sells Wind Bonds.

Figure 27.3: Utility-scale wind farm.

Setting Size

The majority of people want to resolve climate change. Subsequently, new laws that require decarbonization will probably appear this decade. It is likely these would increase solar farm and wind farm construction. For example, if government wanted to decarbonize 6% of all electricity each year, and 1% is already being decarbonized by building traditional solar farms and 1% is already being decarbonized by building traditional wind farms, the government might want the NSFS and NWFS combined to contribute at least 4%. In other words, electricity customers might be required to buy more green electricity each year, and the NSFS/NWFS organizations would need to raise money accordingly.

Junk Is a Serious Problem

Let's take a break from economics and talk about electronics. Hardware devices that convert one type of electricity to another type are typically rated for a maximum amount of electrical power. In many cases, a device will not perform long at advertised power. However, manufacturers are compelled to claim high power ratings to be competitive. Subsequently, solar farm owners might be misled into buying hardware that fails prematurely. And this might decrease dividend payments to bond-holders.

The Commissioner Must Block Junk

Electricity customers would want contracts with lower-priced farms. Therefore, owners would be under pressure to keep costs down. However, not too low as to buy junk that fails prematurely. This includes electronics, solar panels, frames that hold panels, underground conduits, and wiring harnesses.

Electricity customers might be inclined to accept contracts with junk since they only pay for electricity received and are not adversely affected by reduced output, reduced profit to the owner, and reduced dividends to investors.

Investors have no way of evaluating when owners should spend money and when they should economize. Therefore, the Commissioner would need to block junk on their behalf and protect the entire NSFS system. To do this, the commissioner would need an office of engineers who understand solar farm construction and use past data to estimate future technical and economic performance.

Let's Run the Numbers

If 2% of U.S. electricity were decarbonized each year via the NSFS, it would need to oversee 35GW of solar power construction each year. If the capacity of each solar farm were 0.5GW, for example, 71 farms would be built each year, where each is approximately 3 x 3 km (2 x 2 miles) in size.

Typical equipment costs are $1.12-per-watt (CAPEX, NREL 2022); therefore, investors would need to put in $39B/yr (35GW x $1.12). Typical electricity costs are 3.7¢/kWh (LCOE, NREL 2022 Class 4, no tax credits, 0.5¢/kWh for power wires). Therefore, revenue would need to be at least $3B/yr to cover costs ($.037 x 35GW x 0.001 x 2334Wh/W/yr). The investment rate of return would depend on several factors, such as profit to owner and electricity price. For details, see the below analysis.

Decarbonization	2.0%	%/yr	% US total electricity decarbonized ea yr
	4,120	TWh/yr	Total electricity consumption, 2021 US EIA
	82	TWh/yr El	Electricity decarbonized each year
	187	TWh/yr Ht	Heat avoided from burning natural gas
Solar Farm	35	GW	Capacity of each solar farm
	$3.0	$B/yr	Electricity cost per year, LCOE, NREL 2022
	34	$MtCO_2$/yr	CO_2 reduced per year (gas not burned)
	$39.5	$B/yr	Solar farm initial equipment cost
Multiple Solar Farms	0.50	GW	Size of each solar farm
	71	count	Number of solar farms
	10	sq km	Square kilometers per solar farm
Solar Farm Costs	$1.120	$/Watt	Solar farm inital cost, CAPEX, NREL 2022
	$0.037	$/kWh El	Electricity cost, LCOE, NREL 2022 Class 4,
			no tax credits, $0.005/kWh power wires
	2,334	kWh/kW	Annual production, NREL 2022 Class 4
Natural Gas Power	$4.00	$/mcf	Cost of natural gas, wholesale, typ. price
	0.000413	$mtCO_2$/kWh el	CO_2 emissions from electricity, metric ton
	$3.75	$/GJ	Internal energy within natural gas
	$0.014	$/kWh Ht	Cost of heat energy in natural gas
	44%	%	Efficiency of gas power plant
	$0.031	$/kWh El	Cost of natural gas per unit of electricity
Additional Cost	$0.006	$/kWh El	Additional cost green electricity
(solar instead of gas)	$0.53	$B/yr	Additional cost green electricity
	$15	$/mtCO_2$	Decarbonization cost, $-per-m-ton-$CO_2$
	330	M	U.S. population
	$1.59	$/person/yr	Decarbonization cost-per-person-per-yr

Figure 27.4: The economics of decarbonizing 2% of U.S. electricity via 71 solar farms, each 0.5GW in size (Calculations by Weinreb).

The Residential Solar Problem

The cost of electricity from solar panels on houses is 3-times higher than that at solar farms (e.g. 2.6¢/kWh vs. 8.6¢/kWh LCOE). This is due to residential solar incurring the following overhead cost every ~20 panels: multiple quotes, contracting, mechanical design, city approval, electrical design, installation, and inspection. Incidentally, this overhead causes fiscally conservative lawmakers to disfavor government support for residential solar.

Figure 27.5: Residential solar panel installation.

Resolving the Residential Solar Problem

In theory, the electricity billing system for residential and commercial buildings could be connected to the NSFS/NWFS system. Building owners could then invest in solar and wind farms instead of their own buildings.

For example, a homeowner might prefer to give $10K to their power company for 30 panels at a solar farm, instead of giving $10K to a solar installation company that installs 14 panels on their roof. The solar farm panels would produce 1.6-times more electricity per panel due to continuously tilting toward the sun via a motor instead of being stationary.

Solar bonds might appear on a home-owner's electric bill as an asset that pays a monthly dividend determined by solar farm electricity sales. If a homeowner bought $10K of solar bonds, their bill would probably be close to zero for approximately 20 years. Also, they could sell bonds at any time.

Carbon Offsets at Large Scales without Fraud

Investors and farm owners participate to make money, not to reduce CO_2. However, many entities are willing to pay money to reduce CO_2. These are typically referred to as "carbon offsets," and unfortunately, many are fraudulent. Alternatively, if one is looking for real offsets at large scales, the NSFS/NWFS system might be a nice option. More specifically, the system could be used to pay the green premium on someone else's electricity, and flip them off carbon. For example, if coal cost 2.5¢/kWh and green electricity cost 4¢/kWh, a 1.5¢/kWh offset could flip the customer and reduce CO_2 at $15-per-ton ($10 x (4¢ - 2.5¢)).

Who Might Develop this System?

NSFS software does not exist. However, it could be developed to the point of simple prototypes, perhaps for less than $100M.

A company might look at developing this as a proprietary system that they control. However, investors in their venture would probably consider this too much risk. If one component was missing or government regulators were not supportive, revenue would be zero.

Alternatively, a government or philanthropic organization looking to reduce CO_2 might fund development. They might consider this a relatively low-cost method to reduce CO_2 globally. However, most nations do not trust others to manage their national infrastructure. Therefore, they might require open source and control over their commissioner's office, both of which are feasible. Open-source entails placing files on the internet for anyone to copy and modify at no cost. And a philanthropic entity might be inclined to do this to reduce CO_2.

Figure 27.6: Utility-scale solar farm.

Conclusion

A transparent and automated solar farm and wind farm system could potentially reduce cost, reduce risk, and increase construction rates. And a government or foundation could probably get this started with open-source software development.

28. Carbon, Capture and Sequestration (CCS)

Carbon Capture and Sequestration (<u>CCS</u>) is a process by which CO_2 gas is captured and either stored or utilized. CCS is of intense interest for several reasons:

- It reduces CO_2 emissions.

- It helps to maintain the value of carbon-based infrastructure that has already been built and possibly paid for (e.g. coal-fired cement factory).

- It helps to maintain the value of underground carbon-based assets that would otherwise be unburnable due to decarbonization (e.g. coal, oil, and natural gas).

- It provides a way for petroleum companies to utilize their core competencies in a decarbonized world since CCS is mechanically similar to natural gas extraction, only in reverse.

Currently, 40 million tons of CO_2 are processed by CCS each year worldwide (40Mt/yr). However, global CO_2 emissions are approximately 1000 times more. CCS has not progressed further due to cost and a lack of government intervention that forces markets to absorb this additional cost. However, CCS will probably become popular eventually, driven by increased concern over climate change and a reduction of CCS costs.

To scale up CCS, one would need to coordinate: (a) the investigation of storage sites, (b) the construction of CO_2 piping networks, and (c) modifications to existing carbon-based infrastructure. Synchronizing these requires a long-term strategy that understands how CCS is likely to unfold and plans accordingly.

What Is Carbon Capture and Sequestration?

CCS consists of three steps: Capture, Transport, and Storage.

- **Capture** involves extracting CO_2 from a stream of gas. For example, one can extract CO_2 from the exhaust of a facility that burns natural gas to produce electricity. Before capture, approximately 10% of this exhaust is CO_2, while the rest is mostly nitrogen. Capture entails separating the CO_2 from the nitrogen.

- **Transport** typically involves moving CO_2 in pipes.

- **Storage** entails placing CO_2 underground or using it in some way. The cost of storage is often a small percentage of the total CCS cost.

The cost of extraction increases as the CO_2 in the source becomes more dilute. For example, it is easier to extract CO_2 from ethanol production with 85% CO_2 exhaust (~$15/mtCO_2$ extraction cost) than to extract from natural gas-fired electricity generation with 10% CO_2 exhaust (~$60/mtCO_2$). Even more difficult is Direct-Air-Capture (DAC), which involves extracting CO_2 from the atmosphere. Air contains 0.042% (420ppm) CO_2 and extraction costs several hundred $/mtCO_2$.

To store, one typically converts CO_2 gas to a liquid with ≥72 atm (1058 psi) pressure, and injects the liquid 800 meters or more below the surface. One injects to sites that already have fluids at these pressures, which indicates they can hold pressure. Existing oil and natural gas fields are often good candidates since their underground dynamics are already well understood.

When one compresses CO_2 into a liquid, volume decreases 3000-to-1, and density becomes similar to water (i.e. one cubic meter weighs approximately one metric ton). In theory, one could store a year's worth of the world's CO_2 in a 21km diameter underground cylinder that is 100m tall ($34Gt/yr$ global $CO_2 = h \times \pi \times r^2 = 100m \times 3.14 \times 10,400m^2$).

What Would It Cost to Capture 30% of the World's CO_2?

The world currently emits approximately $34Gt/yr$ of CO_2. If $10Gt/yr$ were processed via CCS at a cost of $100-per-ton, for example, then the total cost worldwide would be $1T each year ($10G \times $100). If the U.S. handled 16%, cost would be $160B each year after it had been built out to the $1.6Gt/yr$ level. If built over 10 years, the cost would be $16B in year #1, $32B in year #2, and $160B/yr after year #10. The public is not comfortable with these numbers; therefore, R&D is needed to reduce CCS costs.

What Limits CCS Deployment?

CCS at the $10Gt/yr$ scale is not limited by the availability of underground storage, nor is it limited by technology. Instead, it is limited by CCS costs, which vary from \$40 to \$150/mtCO$_2$. The lower numbers apply to processes with higher concentrations of CO_2, such as ethanol production. However, in most CCS applications, costs are in excess of \$100/mtCO$_2$.

When will the World do CCS at Gigaton-per-year scales?

If one replaces carbon-based electrical power generation with electricity from solar and wind farms; the cost to avoid a ton of carbon is typically less than \$50/mtCO$_2$. Therefore, when generating electricity, decarbonizing via solar and wind power is often preferable to CCS.

Many industrial processes consume heat that is generated by burning coal or natural gas. In many cases, CCS is the lowest-cost way to decarbonize these processes since making high-temperature heat with solar or wind power is often more costly. The lowest cost way to decarbonize industrial processes worldwide is probably a high-temperature nuclear reactor in China. However, in many cases, this is not feasible for a variety of reasons.

One can assemble a list of potential solar farms, wind farms and CCS construction projects; and sort by increasing cost-to-avoid-a-ton-of-CO$_2$. Then one can calculate how many projects are needed each year over the next few decades to decarbonize a nation to zero emissions. In many cases, the lowest cost initially would be solar farms and wind farms. However, after decarbonizing most electricity with renewables, one would bump into the easier CCS projects, followed by the more difficult CCS projects.

Laws that require decarbonization are needed to push CCS forward. These laws do not exist. However, as evidence of climate change increases, they become more likely.

When Will the World Do DAC at Gigaton-per-Year scales?

There is no business case at this time for Direct-Air-Capture (DAC) since it costs less to extract CO_2 from dense sources, such as the exhaust from burning coal or natural gas. However, there will come a day when the world stops burning carbon-based fuels, perhaps 50 years from now, and DAC becomes economically viable. And we can do R&D on DAC between now and then, to prepare for that day.

Let's assume we stop emitting CO_2 in 2070, and global temperatures have risen 2° to 3°C. After 2070, this additional temperature will slowly decay over thousands of years. Also, over thousands of years, it will partially melt a 2,000-meter-thick layer of ice that covers the South Pole. This will cause the sea to <u>rise</u> and cover coastal cities. To fight this problem, the world might do DAC over many years, *starting* when CO_2 emissions reach zero and air is the densest source of CO_2 available.

Two CO_2 Problems

In a sense, we are dealing with two CO_2 problems. One is the immediate impact of higher global temperatures that cause the land to become drier. And the other is the long-term problem of melting South Pole ice that causes the sea to rise one to two meters every 100 years. The first problem is addressed by reducing CO_2 emissions over several decades. And the second problem is addressed with DAC, perhaps over hundreds of years, starting several decades from now. One does not do DAC now since extracting CO_2 from a gas that is 0.04% CO_2 cost more than extracting CO_2 from a gas that is 10% CO_2. And one does not do large scale CCS at this time since it costs less to build a solar farm.

Nations Need a Long-Term CCS Strategy

A reasonable CCS strategy assumes government intervention eventually pushes decarbonization forward in increasing cost-to-avoid-a-ton-of-CO_2 order and prepares accordingly. Preparation can be broken into several types:

- Increase R&D that reduces the cost of capture, transport, and storage.

- Build databases of potential decarbonization projects that include CCS.

- Build models that design piping networks that transport CO_2 from sources to storage.

- Build systems that track the production, distribution, and consumption of green commodities. This includes electricity, chemicals & materials.

For details, see <u>*What is our Long Term CCS Strategy?*</u> *(Power Electronics, Jan 2022).*

29. Cover Buildings with Solar Skin

In theory, a billion dollar-sized R&D initiative could potentially develop machines that fabricate, install and maintain custom pieces of PV solar material that wrap building roof and wall surfaces at a cost less than traditional coverings. Costing less is potentially feasible since side clapboards and roof shingles are installed by hand, and solar skin could be automated. If solar costs less than traditional coverings, it could be driven forward by consumers who favor paying less.

Figure 29.1: Illustration of custom PV solar skin that mounts directly onto plywood and wraps features such as windows and doors (Concept illustration by Weinreb).

Custom Solar Fits Together Like a Puzzle

The typical house places drywall on internal wall surfaces and places plywood on external wall surfaces. Workers typically begin with solid 4 x 8ft (1.2 x 2.4m) panels and cut them into custom shapes that wrap windows and doors. To make this easier, architectural software generates drawings of each piece.

In theory, one could do something similar with solar material that directly attaches to external plywood. For example, one could wrap a building with

12 *custom* pieces, as illustrated <u>below</u>. In this concept, pieces are outlined in green and numbered; horizontal rails that secure material to external plywood are shown in blue, and brackets that provide a watertight seal at window/door vertical edges are shown in violet.

Figure 29.2: Custom pieces of solar fit together like a puzzle (Concept illustration by Weinreb).

Solar cannot be cut in the field due to internal wires; therefore, machines would be needed to fabricate custom shapes in a factory. The placement of windows and doors relative to drawings is often only accurate to ±1cm. Therefore, photography, video, or laser scanning would be needed to improve accuracy.

Newly constructed buildings might incorporate windows/doors with standardized features that mechanically interface to solar material. Alternatively, existing construction might utilize custom factory-made brackets. A building lasts much longer than PV solar; therefore, solar skin would need to support disassembly and replacement, via bolts and screws.

Horizontal Rails Secure Solar Skin to Surface

The figure below shows an example of a horizontal seam between two pieces of solar skin. This seam is illustrated above in blue. A lower rail (violet) attaches to plywood via screws, and an upper rail (light green) attaches to the lower rail via bolts. Flexible ~2mm thick PV solar material (dark blue) attaches to rails via an adhesive (yellow). An optional embedded Printed Circuit Board (PCB) (dark green) supports electronic components ~1cm tall (dark red), and a lower layer of thin sheet metal (gray) presses against plywood (brown). This provides strength and a fire barrier. Not shown is the honeycomb plastic between the lower metal layer and upper solar layer that fills empty space around PCB. Rain-water (bright red) flows across overlapped joints, and avoids plywood.

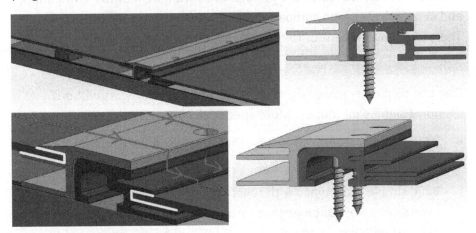

Figure 29.3: Concept illustration of horizontal rails that secure solar material with a watertight seal (Source: UMass Open-Source Solar Design Team sponsored by Manhattan 2).

Why Has This Not Been Done?

The good news is PV silicon and thin-film materials cost relatively little. And developing a mechanical system that wraps a building costs little. The bad news is developing commercial-grade machines that fabricate and install custom pieces would be costly. Also, multiple complicated machines causes investors to consider this "too big" or "too many moving parts," which it is.

Subsequently, government or foundation funding would be needed to move this forward.

R&D Strategy

There are many ways to wrap a building, each of which can be characterized with several parameters: type of building, new construction or existing, roof or wall, solar material physical topology (e.g. large rollable, large flat, small flat), embedded electronics or not, 3mm flat glass or flexible plastic cover, and silicon or thin-film PV.

Designing the mechanics of a solar skin system, and constructing a one cubic meter sized prototype would cost little money. However, developing automated machines that fabricate and install could cost hundreds of millions of dollars or more.

Interconnection standards are needed to coordinate multiple companies, and in many cases, one company cannot afford to develop these. Therefore, government or foundation support would be needed.

Getting Started With a "Small" Budget

One can do paper-only designs and build simple prototypes without spending significant money. More specifically, one can:

- Design and prototype hardware that provides a water-tight seal at vertical and horizontal joints.

- Build simple prototypes with several pieces of solar material that overlap at a horizontal edge, or interface with a window vertical edge, and test with wind and water.

- Build a one cubic meter sized "house" out of plywood, wrap it with pieces of solar skin made by hand, and test it with wind and water. One can initially work with sheets of plastics (not PV material) and focus on creating a watertight system that attaches to plywood, wraps windows and doors, and supports disassembly. A one cubic meter box with one window and one door would probably be sufficient.

For more details, see *How to Cover Buildings with Solar Skins* (*Power Electronics, Feb 2022*).

30. Automate Solar on Buildings

A house needs a significant amount of PV solar to be a net producer of electricity, especially when heating with electricity in a cold climate. For this reason, one might fully cover an oversized roof edge-to-edge, as illustrated <u>below</u>. This concept illustrates a 1:1 floor-to-solar ratio (i.e. both are 185m²). If one examines this carefully, one might notice half the roof is not above the structure.

Figure 30.1: Oversized roof supports significantly more solar than a typical residential solar installation (Concept by architect <u>John Meyer</u>).

Making an *oversized* roof economically viable is a challenge since large structures similar to that shown above tend to be costly. However, engineers might be able to make this work financially by extending a traditional roof with light factory-made framing, as illustrated <u>below</u>.

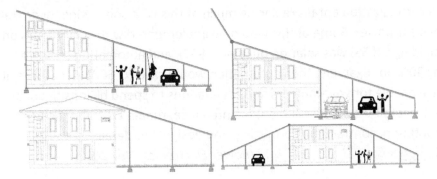

Figure 30.2: External metal framing supports large amounts of solar (Concept illustration by Weinreb).

Reduce Costs with Standardized Sub-Assemblies and Machines

To reduce the cost of solar panels mounted on metal framing, engineers could explore modular systems that support: (a) multiple factories that mass produce standardized sub-assemblies, (b) transportation systems that stack sub-assemblies in shipping containers, and (c) automated installation via custom machines.

Figure 30.3. Standardized sub-assemblies with automated assembly (Concept illustration by Weinreb).

Automate Solar Installation on Buildings

The average US resident pays $2.81-per-watt to install PV solar panels on their house. However, the panels themselves only cost $0.27-per-watt wholesale in China. This means 90% of the costs are for things other than panel manufacturing ($2.54 / $2.81).

The world currently spends $3.4T/yr on electricity generation and distribution, which works out to $100T if spent over 30 years ($3.4T x 30). Decarbonization entails replacing much of this with solar, wind, hydro, and nuclear power. Some of this would be implemented with solar panels on buildings. If 5% was solar on buildings ($5T), and automation reduced this by 30%, for example, then automation would save $1,500B. Therefore, it is reasonable for governments and foundations to spend billions of dollars to automate PV solar installation, maintenance, repair, customer acquisition, quotation, contracting, permitting, and design. For details, see *Why Spend $1B on Solar Installation R&D?* (*Power Electronics, Nov 2021*).

31. Mechanize Solar on Land

Agricultural farms were maintained by hand for thousands of years until they were mechanized with tractors. Today, we maintain solar farms mostly by hand, but in theory, they could be mechanized too.

The world is looking at spending trillions of dollars on solar farms. Therefore, it is reasonable to spend billions of dollars to automate, to reduce this cost. Obviously, one would first spend small money and verify feasibility, before spending big money.

It is unlikely that a company would do the initial design since they would consider this too big. However, governments and foundations might be inclined to develop a next-generation solar farm that uses machines to install, maintain, clean, and mass-produce solar material.

Solar Direct to Soil

Solar farms typically mount silicon solar cells 1.5m (4.5ft) above ground. Alternatively, one might unroll flexible thin-film ~2mm (0.1") thick solar material directly onto soil in a manner similar to unrolling a 2m x 100m (6 x 300ft) carpet onto a surface. Prior to installation, the land would be shaped with earth-moving equipment under computer control.

Initially, this might seem like a bad idea. However, there are good reasons for going to ground, such as significantly less material usage. Engineers could explore various techniques for overcoming challenges such as soil erosion, upward pressure due to wind, and keeping material clean.

Traditional PV solar farms use aluminum and glass to resist wind loads. Alternatively, direct-to-soil would use soil for rigidity and use thin-film conversion material instead of silicon solar cells. Thin-film is typically rollable, resistant to hailstones, and does not need 3.2mm (0.12") thick protective flat tempered glass. It also has less conversion efficiency and more efficiency degradation per year, which means one needs more land for the same energy output. However, if one has an infinite supply of land, they might focus on cost-per-watt as opposed to cost-per-square meter of land.

The above-ground layer might be similar to flat flexible plastic with an embedded steel wire mesh. To hold in place, installation machinery might install a parallel layer of material underground, perhaps 50cm (20") below the top above-ground layer. The above-ground layer might connect to the underground anchoring layer via metal links.

Some regions would be more feasible than others. For example, deserts with 3cm (1") rain per month, and dense soil, might be most suitable. Engineers would need 30-year simulations and wind tunnel testing to ensure that soil movement due to wind and rain is acceptable.

Currently, silicon-based solar panels are mass-produced and cost less than thin-film. However, direct-to-soil uses less metal, glass, and concrete; and thin-film PV is easier to fabricate than silicon solar cells. Therefore, direct-to-soil thin-film would probably cost less if mass-produced. Also, it would consume significantly less material and emit less CO_2 due to less material fabrication.

Machines that shape land might look similar to earth-moving equipment, and machines that clean might look similar to agricultural sprinklers yet with less water, examples are which are pictured below.

Figure 31.1. Earth-moving vehicles and agricultural sprinkler system.

Further Reading

For details on how this might work, see the following articles published in Power Electronics in 2021.

- *Mechanizing PV Solar on Land*
- *Turning Deserts into Factories*
- *How to Solve the Climate Change Problem with Solar Farms*

32. Automate the Construction of Power Transmission Towers

It is easier to transport coal or natural gas fuel to a power generation plant near a city, than to generate electricity faraway and move the electricity on power wires. However, placing power sources next to consumers is sometimes not convenient when working with solar farms, wind farms, and hydroelectric dams. For example, Colorado might rely on local wind farms when windy in Colorado, and rely on faraway solar farms in Arizona when it is sunny in Arizona. Or Colorado might rely on wind farms in faraway Texas when it is calm in Colorado and windy in Texas. In other words, decarbonization requires significantly more long-distance power wires.

Upgrading Power Lines

Getting land for new power wires is sometimes difficult. Therefore, a government office with authority to rebuild existing power wires on a wider tract of land would be helpful. If one replaces three 2.5cm diameter cables with eight 5cm diameter cables and increases voltage 5-fold, power transmitted increases 50-fold, for example. This requires removing existing towers, increasing land tract width, and building new towers.

Figure 32.1: Traditional power cables (left) and jumbo-sized ultra-high-voltage cables (right).

Get Ready For Jumbo-Sized Power Transmission

Jumbo-sized power transmission (pictured above right) requires stronger towers, taller towers, and sophisticated ultra-high-voltage electronics. Currently, jumbo is only prevalent in China. However, this will probably change when other nations make more use of distant sources of green electricity.

The state of New York typically requires 40GW of power, and each jumbo-sized line typically carries 8GW. Therefore, powering the entire state would require 5 jumbos (40GW / 8GW). However, solar and wind sources are intermittent. Therefore, more lines would be needed to support variable sources.

Automate Power Transmission Tower Assembly

Expanding the grid will cost trillions of dollars worldwide over several decades. Therefore, it is reasonable to spend billions of additional dollars on R&D, to reduce this cost. For example, one might explore machines that automate the building of power towers using industrial robots mounted on trucks, as illustrated below. For details, see *How to Reduce the Cost of Electrical Power Transmission (Power Electronics, Sept 2021).*

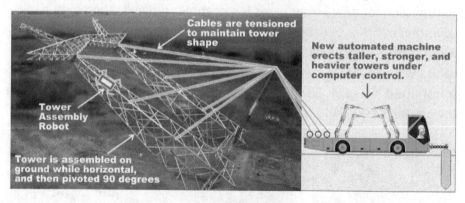

Figure 32.2: Machine automates the assembly of power transmission towers (Concept illustration by Weinreb).

33. Decarbonize the Heating of Buildings

Many buildings are heated by burning natural gas in a furnace. This heats metal fins within a duct, which heats the air that circulates throughout the building. Alternatively, one can install a system that creates heat using electricity.

There are two primary ways to produce heat with electricity. One is a heat pump, and the other is a simple electrical heating element. The heat pump is 2 to 4 times more efficient than the heating element. For example, one can feed 1 watt into a heat pump and get 4 watts of heat; or feed 1 watt into a simple heating element and get 1 watt of heat. One can get more out of the heat pump since it moves heat from one place to another instead of creating it. When heating a building, heat pumps move heat from outside the building to inside. And this causes outdoor air to become colder. Heat pumps are already inside air conditioners. Therefore, they can be used to heat buildings, to an extent, with little additional equipment cost.

In most cases, the electricity that feeds a heat pump is made by burning natural gas or coal at a power plant, and this facility emits CO_2. One might prefer "green" electricity, made without emitting CO_2. However, additional green electricity for buildings is often not available.

A building's energy cost often increases when it switches from a natural gas furnace to a heat pump, especially when outdoor temperatures are very cold. This is due to the fact that a heat pump's efficiency decreases when outdoor temperatures decrease.

Gas Furnace vs. Electric Heat Pump

Buildings typically obtain heat from a gas furnace or an electric heat pump, and it is impossible to generalize which of these costs less or emits less CO_2. This is due to multiple factors that vary over time and place. For example, the efficiency of a heat pump is a function of outside air temperature. And the spot price of both natural gas and electricity vary throughout the day and between regions.

Unfortunately, the size of the heat pump needed for a very cold day tends to be larger than that needed for a hot summer day. For example, the typical air conditioner on a 38°C summer day moves heat 14°C (38°C to 24°C), and the typical heating system on a -18°C winter day moves heat 42°C (-18°C to 24°C). The latter is 3-times further and therefore requires a much larger and more costly heat pump. To reduce the need for costly heat pumps, one can operate a gas furnace and a heat pump concurrently on very cold days.

National HVAC Communications and Control

There are many ways to decarbonize building heat. However, to get this done at the lowest cost, one would probably need standardized communications between buildings, regional computers, and national computers. This currently does not exist; however, it could be developed. For details, see *How to Decarbonize the Heating of Buildings at Lowest Cost* *(Power Electronics, June 2022)*.

Thermal Storage

Thermal storage typically entails placing a tank of water in a building, heating or cooling it with cheap or clean energy (e.g. green electricity), and then using it later when energy is less cheap or less clean. For example, if a wind farm at 3 am is discarding electricity due to being in saturation (e.g. no natural gas is being burned to produce grid electricity), then one might store heat or cold in a tank and use it later when green electricity is not available.

Reduce Cost of Installing Ground Source

Underground soil is typically at a ~14°C (58°F) temperature, and if one embeds pipes into that soil and circulates water through those pipes, they can get water at that temperature. If one circulates this water through a heat pump, they can reduce electricity consumption approximately 2-fold when heating and cooling. This technique is referred to as a "ground source heat pump" (GSHP), and it has two disadvantages. It consumes land, and installing underground piping is costly (e.g. $20K per house). Therefore, engineers should explore reducing the installation cost with automated machines.

34. Develop Next Generation Buildings

To fully automate buildings, one would need to place a microprocessor chip in every device and connect all devices with reliable communication. Devices include things like light switches, light sockets, HVAC equipment, appliances, motorized dampers in ducts, fans in ducts, motorized valves in radiators, thermal storage tanks, motors that move thermal covers over windows, occupancy sensors, temperature sensors, and fire detectors.

This would enable one to control the temperature of each room, move heat from one room to another, move heat between rooms and thermal storage, and move heat between rooms and underground soil. As noted previously, one can run pipes underground to get approximately 14°C (58°F), and this can be used to significantly reduce HVAC energy consumption.

Open Source Operating System

To ensure coordination, all devices would probably need to run the same operating system. Companies and countries would only accept this if it were open source (i.e. no one owns it). An example is BuildingBus, developed by Glenn Weinreb in 2021. He has developed approximately 30 automation and control systems over the last 43 years and is, therefore, one of the world's experts in this field.

Reliable Communication

When one turns on a physical wall light switch, the communication between the switch and the ceiling bulb is operational ≥ 99.999% ("5 nine's") of the time. It's a subtle point that gets little attention yet is important. Occupants do not accept less reliability from common building infrastructure. It's worth noting that wireless and power-line communication is significantly less reliable, with failure rates on the order of 1%. To get 99.999% reliability within a building, one would probably need to include a communications data wire in power cables embedded in walls. The additional cost of this wire would be small.

Light and Heavy Devices

One might divide devices into two categories: Light and Heavy. Light might consume less than 20W of power, and heavy devices would consume more. Light might include things like light bulbs, light switches, sensors, and small motors. And Heavy might include things like 110/220 V_{AC} power outlets, HVAC equipment, large appliances, and large motors. Most devices in a building are Light and, therefore, could be powered by smaller cables with lower voltages and fewer safety requirements. In other words, a building might have a network of light devices powered by 48 V_{DC} and one communications wire. It might have another network of Heavy devices powered by 110/220 V_{AC} and two data wires. The Heavy devices might route thick power wires in metal conduit, whereas the Light devices might use smaller cables without conduit.

Plug-and-Play Standards are Needed

To support plug-and-play connectivity, one would need to develop interconnection standards that define how devices connect electrically, mechanically, and with data communications. Before proposing a standard, one must develop, prototype, test, and debug the system. And this might cost tens of millions of dollars, assuming the money is controlled by talented engineers, and open source is required by the funding source. Companies cannot afford this, and governments tend not to provide this kind of leadership. Therefore, a foundation would probably be needed to move this forward. The Gates Foundation would be uniquely suited since Bill Gates has experience developing operating systems and interconnection standards (e.g. UPnP).

Further Reading Regarding Building Automation

- *Using processors and software to make buildings smarter*
- *Standards Are Needed to Thermally Cover Windows*
- *Standards are Needed to Fully Control Air in Buildings*
- *How to Decarbonize the Heating of Buildings at Lowest Cost*
- *Manhattan 2 Open-Source Smart Building Development*
- *Manhattan 2 Open-Source Window Thermal Cover Development*
- *Manhattan 2 Open-Source Fan/Damper Development*

Epilogue

Those concerned about climate change might feel like they are stuck in a bad dream. Like being chased in the forest at 3am and unable to break free. The threat is obvious, yet little is being done. What is happening?

Below is a brief summary regarding the United States.

- Decarbonization to zero emissions will not occur unless required by law, and this law does not exist.
- Moving this law forward would require a political coalition that benefits. For example, states that import carbon-based fuels benefit from decarbonization in two ways: (a) they gain local green jobs while carbon jobs are lost elsewhere, and (b) they save money when decarbonization causes fuel price to drop, due to less consumption.
- Individuals, companies, cities and states are often encouraged to reduce CO_2. However, they rarely have the physical ability to do so at low cost. This is mostly due to overhead costs at each "small" project.
- Past decarbonization efforts have been mild. Alternatively, to get to zero over several decades, the world would need to do massive construction at unprecedented scales. This might sound expensive; however, infrastructure is typically paid for with borrowed money. And loans are repaid with revenue generated by the infrastructure.
- Power companies are capable of decarbonizing electricity at massive scales and at low cost.
- Websites that model the costs and impact of decarbonization initiatives are lacking. Consequently, journalists and lawmakers often operate blindly, and money rarely flows to where it is needed most.
- Current decarbonization policy is driven by domestic manufacturers who use climate change to further their financial interests.
- The fossil fuel industries and their friends oppose decarbonization legislation by spending money on lobbyists and donations. However, the largest obstacle seems to be the failure of government leaders to understand they are being led by domestic manufacturers who have no interest in getting to zero over several decades at the lowest-cost.

Our failure to act is a classic case of the tail wagging the dog.

Final Note from Author

This book might seem critical of manufacturing and petroleum engineers; however, it is not my intent to be negative. I have worked extensively with these engineers for forty years and for the most part, they are good people, they are smart, they care about their planet, and they want prosperity for all. Also, they must keep costs down to compete. And, if government requires their competitors to incur an additional expense, they can afford it too.

Power Company engineers know how to decarbonize, yet will not proceed without a mandate from government. And government engineers know how to set up a mandate, yet will not proceed without instructions from government leaders.

Government leaders are surrounded by domestic manufacturers (my friends) who state "let me fix this". However, these companies are focused on their own financial interests, not getting to zero at the lowest cost.

To resolve climate change, government leaders need to do two things: (a) work with political coalitions that benefit from getting to zero at the lowest cost, and (b) plant the right seeds in the right places, as discussed in the "Decarbonization Act of 202x" chapter.

Author Biography

Glenn Weinreb is the Director of the Manhattan 2 Project, a non-profit that does research on how to resolve climate change at the lowest cost and in a way that is politically feasible.

Weinreb founded GW Instruments while a student at MIT in the 1980's. This company designs and manufactures products that automate factories and research laboratories. And over forty years, almost every day, he interacted with manufacturing engineers and research scientists at thousands of different organizations.

One morning in 2019 Weinreb awoke with an epiphany. He felt his job was meaningless, and he wanted to do something different. He was tired of chasing money as an entrepreneur, and he instead wanted to help the planet. He thought about how his background was unique and gave him a different perspective on energy, manufacturing and R&D. So he formed The Manhattan 2 Project with some friends. And between 2019 and 2022 he sponsored and managed 25 university R&D students, and published 30 articles on climate change solutions.

For a TEDx talk that summarizes this book in 10 minutes, search "a plan to save the planet" at TED.com. And for a CBS news segment that discusses some of Glenn's work, search "sesL3id7hba" at YouTube.com.

Contact the Author

To contact the author, email gWeinreb (at) manhattan2.org